The Gospel of Matthew

Comprehensive Workbook

P.O. Box D, Coeur d'Alene, Idaho 83816-0347 1-800-546-8731

How to Use this Workbook

For maximum benefit, please read the following tips:

1. Before starting a *Book of Matthew* session, please read through the study questions and, if part of a Small Group, the discussion questions that pertain to that session.

2. The first section of each session is designed to help you take notes. You will discover that there is much more information than space provided, so it may be helpful to have extra paper on which to write.

3. If you are a Small Group leader, please feel free to use the questions at the back of the workbook to facilitate discussion within your group. See the *Discussion Questions for Small Group Leaders* section.

4. Through arrangements with Louisiana Baptist University, we can offer you the means to earn college course credit toward a LBU degree up to and including the Ph.D. through Koinonia Institute. If you are interested in obtaining college credit for this study course(s), you will need to follow these steps:

    a. Go to (www.studycenter.com/downloads/ki_info_kit.pdf) to download an application packet which, which includes applications to both KI and LBU (.pdf files), and the link to LBU's online catalog (www.lbu.edu). A list of available courses through KI is available at www.studycenter.com/courses.
    b. Fill out both applications and return with your $100 registration fee, which enrolls you in both KI and LBU. LBU will accept all KI course transcripts and is the institute that will grant your degree (you will still need to take distance-learning classes through LBU to earn your degree).
    c. For more information concerning transcript and LBU credit transfer costs, email (registrar@studycenter.com)
    d. This study is actually two college courses: BIB 529-1: Matthew I (Sessions 1-12) and BIB 529-2: Matthew II (Sessions 13-24).
    e. For more information on the Online Course procedures, see the information page at the Koinonia Institute section at the back of this workbook.

5. For more information on Koinonia Institute's Medallion Program and for costs regarding our Campus Access Pass (CAP) which allows you to take all your K-House Courses tuition-free, please email the Koinonia Institute Registrar at registrar@studycenter.com.

Session 1

The Gospel of

Matthew

Introduction
&
Chapter 1

Canon Complete?

Old Testament:

Unexplained Ceremonies	(Sacrificial Rituals)
Unachieved Purposes	(Covenants)
Unappeased Longings	(Poetical books)
Unfulfilled Prophecies	(over 7,000…)

Oldest Known Manuscript

- Dr. Carsten Thiede, using a scanning laser microscope, and comparing with four other manuscripts,
  - at Qumran (dated to 58 AD)
  - at Herculaneum (dated prior to 79 AD)
  - at Masada (dated to between 73-74 AD)
  - At Egyptian town of Oxyrynchus (65-66 AD)
- Has concluded that this is either an original of Matthew's Gospel, or an immediate copy, written while Matthew and the other disciples and other eyewitnesses were still alive.

Authentication Codes?

- An automatic security monitor, watching over every single letter of the text, that doesn't rust or wear out, running continually over several thousand years…
- Fingerprint signature of the Author
- Non-compromiseable design

Sevens in the Bible

- Occur in over 600 passages
  - Some overt
  - Some structural
  - Some hidden
- Underlying Heptadic Structures as a signature?

Heptadic Structures

- Vocabulary: 72 words
- Gematrical values:

Total:	42,364	=	7	x	6,052
α – β	9,821	=	7	x	1,403
γ – δ	1,904	=	7	x	272
ϵ – ξ	3,703	=	7	x	529
θ – ρ	19,264	=	7	x	2,752
σ – χ	7,672	=	7	x	1,096

Childhood of Christ

(Matthew 2)

Vocabulary: 161 = 7 x 23

Letters: 896 = 7 x 128

Forms: 238 = 7 x 34

Values:

Vocabulary: 123,529 = 7 x 17,647

Forms: 166,985 = 7 x 23,855

(Also: 4 divisions, 3 speakers, etc. have similar structures)

Chances of Multiples of 7

For 2	7^2 = (7 x 7)	49
For 3	7^3 = (7 x 7 x 7)	343
For 4	7^4 = (7 x 7 x 7 x 7) etc.	2,401
For 5	7^5	16,807
For 6	7^6	117,649
For 7	7^7	823,543
For 8	7^8	5,764,801
For 9	7^9	40,353,607
For 10	7^{10}	282,475,249
For 11	7^{11}	1,977,326,743
For 12	7^{12}	13,841,287,201
For 13	7^{13}	96,889,010,047
For 14	7^{14}	678,223,072,849
For 15	7^{15}	4,747,561,509,943
For 16	7^{16}	33,232,930,569,601
For 17	7^{17}	232,630,513,987,207

Comprehensive Design

New Testament consists of 27 books;

Terminations: each book begins and ends with a word: 2 x 27 = 54 words:

Total vocabulary of 28 (7 x 4)

in the Gospels 7 (7 x 1)

Total gematrical value 46,949 (7 x 6707)

Value of the shortest word, ὁ, 70 (7 x 10)

Value of longest word, ἀποκάλυψις,

1512 (7 x 6 x 6 x 6)

Inter-Testament Heptadic Bridges

	OT +	NT =	Total	
"Hallelujah"	24	4	28	7 x 4
"Hosanna"	1	6	7	7 x 1
"Shepherd"	12	9	21	7 x 3
"Jehovah Sabaoth"	285	2	287	7 x 41
"Corban"	82	2	84	7 x 12
"Milk"	44	5	49	7 x 7
"Isaac"	112	14	126	7 x 18
"Aaron"	443	5	448	7 x 64
"Abaddon"	6	1	7	7 x 1
"Christ at the right hand of God"	2	19	21	7 x 3
"After Melchizedek"	1	6	7	7 x 1
"Stone ...refused...headstone..."	1	6	7	7 x 1
"Love thy neighbor as thyself"	1	6	7	7 x 1
"Uncircumcision of the heart"	6	1	7	7 x 1

The Strange Prophecy

And let thy house be like the house of Pharez, whom Tamar bare unto Judah, of the seed which the LORD shall give theeof this young woman.

Ruth 4:12

A bastard shall not enter into the congregation of the LORD; even to his tenth generation shall he not enter into the congregation of the LORD.

Deuteronomy 23:2

1. Perez
2. Hezron
3. Ram
4. Amminadab
5. Nahshon
6. Salmon
7. Boaz
8. Obed
9. Jesse
10. David

Levirite Marriage

- (from Latin *levir,* "husband's brother")
- Codified in the *Torah* — Deut. 25:5-10
- The role of the *Goel*
  - The Kinsman-Redeemer — Ruth 1-4
  - The Ultimate Redemption — Rev 5

And Jesse begat David the king; and David the king begat Solomon of her *that had been the wife* of Urias;
And Solomon begat Roboam; and Roboam begat Abia; and Abia begat Asa;
And Asa begat Josaphat; and Josaphat begat Joram; and Joram begat Ozias;
And Ozias begat Joatham; and Joatham begat Achaz; and Achaz begat Ezekias;
And Ezekias begat Manasses; and Manasses begat Amon; and Amon begat Josias;

Matthew 1:6-10

- Ahaziah slain by Jehu — 2 Kings 9
- Joash slain by servant — 2 Kings 12
- Amaziah slain by Jerusalem — 2 Kings 14

The LORD will not spare him, but then the anger of the LORD and his jealousy shall smoke against that man, and all the curses that are written in this book shall lie upon him, and the LORD shall blot out his name from under heaven.

Deuteronomy 29:20

The House of David

Matthew:

Solomon
Rehoboam
Abijah
Asa
Jehoshaphat
Jehoram
Ahaziah*
Joash*
Amaziah*
Uzziah
Jotham
Ahaz
Hezekiah
Manasseh
Amon
Josiah
Jehoiakim*
Jehoiachin*
Salathiel**
Zerubbabel
Abiud
Eliakim
Azor
Sadoc
Achim
Eliud
Eleazar
Matthan
Jacob
Joseph

Luke:

Nathan
Mattatha
Menan
Melea
Eliakim
Jonan
Joseph
Juda
Simeon
Levi
Matthat
Jorim
Eliezer
Jose
Er
Elmodam
Cosam
Addi
Melchi
Neri
Salathiel**
Zerubbabel
Rhesa
Joanna
Juda
Joseph
Semei
Mattathias
Maath
Nagge
Esli
Naum
Amos
Mattathias
Joseph
Janna
Melchi
Levi
Matthat
Heli
(Mary)

The Coming One

- The 2nd Adam
- A prophet like Moses
- A priest like Melchizedek
- A champion like Joshua
- An offering like Isaac
- A king like David
- A wise counselor like Solomon
- A beloved, rejected, exalted son like Joseph

Specifications Fulfilled

- He would be born of a virgin Isaiah 7:14
  - And He was Matt 1:18-25
- He would be born in Bethlehem Micah 5:2
  - And He was Matt 2:1-6
- He would be taken into Egypt Hosea 11:1
  - And He was Matt 2:15

- He would heal the sick and make people whole Isa 53
  - And He did Matt 8
- He would be crucified Psa 22:14-17
  - And He was Matt 27:31
- He would die for our sins Isa 53
  - And He did John 1:29; 11:49-52
- He would be raised from the dead Psa 16:10
  - And He was Matt 28:1-10

Matthew- SESSION 1: Introduction & Chapter 1

1) In what four ways is the Old Testament ***incomplete***?

2) What four conspicuous omissions in the Gospels imply an early date of their writings?

3) Why do we suspect that Matthew had shorthand skills?

4) What characteristics of Christ's genealogy make it virtually impossible to counterfeit?

5) Name two places that the genealogy of David appears prior to the time of Samuel.

6) List the following Bible references: a) Where in the Old Testament does it hint that the Messiah would be born of a virgin? b) Where in the Old Testament does it *prophesy* that the Messiah must be born of a virgin? c) Where in the Old Testament does it *require* that the Messiah must be born of a virgin?

7) How did the exception granted to Zelophehad impact the Messianic line?

8) What do we know about Matthew's personal life and habits?

9) Highlight two parables that Jesus presented at Matthew's house party.

10) What makes the number of vocabulary words which are unique to the Gospel of Matthew significant? The Gospel of Mark? The Gospel of Luke? The Gospel of John? Why are these significant?

Preparation for the Next Session:

Read Matthew Chapter 2:

Who were the Magi?

Why was "all of Jerusalem troubled" by their presence?

What do we know about Jesus' sojourn in Egypt?

Why did the priests march though the streets of Jerusalem in sackcloth in 7 AD?

Group Discussion Questions: See the *Small Group Leaders* section of this workbook

Session 2

The Gospel of

Matthew

Chapter 2

The Design of the Gospels

	Matthew	Mark	Luke	John
Presents as:	Messiah	Servant	Son of Man	Son of God
Genealogy:	Abraham (Legal)	--	Adam (Blood line)	Eternal (Preexistence)
What Jesus	Said	Did	Felt	Was
To the:	Jew	Roman	Greek	Church
1st Miracle:	Leper cleansed (Jew = sin)	Demon expelled	Demon expelled	Water to Wine
Ends with	Resurrection	Ascension	Promise of Spirit: Acts	Promise of Return: Revelation
Camp Side:	East	West	South	North
Ensign:	Judah	Ephraim	Reuben	Dan
Face:	**Lion**	**Ox**	**Man**	**Eagle**
Style:	Groupings	Snapshots	Narrative	Mystical

Magian Religion vs. Judaism

- Each had its monotheistic concept of one beneficent creator, author of all good, who in turn was opposed by a malevolent evil spirit;
- Each had its hereditary priesthood which became the essential mediator between God and man by virtue of a blood sacrifice;
- Each depended upon the wisdom of the priesthood in divination;
- Each held concepts of clean and unclean forms of life;
- Each involved a *hereditary* priesthood, serving several religions;
- Magi were the priestly caste during Seleucid, Parthian, and Sasanian periods.

Political Background

Since the days of Daniel, the fortunes of both the Persia and the Jewish nation had been closely intertwined:

- Both nations had in their turn falling under Seleucid domination in the wake of Alexander's conquests.
- Both had regained their independence:
  - the Jews under Maccabean leadership,
  - the Persians as the dominating ruling group within the Parthian empire.
- It was at this time that the Magi, in their dual priestly and governmental offices, composed the upper house of the council of the Megistanes ("magistrates") whose duties included the absolute choice and election of the king of the realm.

The Parthian Empire

- Parthia, ancient empire of Asia, in what are now Iran and Afghanistan.
- The Parthians were of Scythian descent, and adopted Median dress and Aryan speech.
- Parthia was subject successively to the Assyrians, Medes, Persians, and Macedonians under Alexander the Great, and then the Seleucids.

The Parthian Empire

- 250 BC: the Parthians succeeded in founding an independent kingdom
- During the 1st century BC, grew into an empire extending from the Euphrates River to the Indus River and from the Oxus (now Amu Darya) River to the Indian Ocean.

Judea: a Buffer Zone

- After the middle of the 1st century BC Parthia was, thus, a rival of Rome, and several wars occurred between the two powers.
- Pompey, the first Roman conqueror of Jerusalem, in 63 B.C. had attacked the Armenian outpost of Parthia.

A Precarious Visit?

- At this time that the Magi, in their dual priestly and governmental office, composed the upper house of the council of the Magistanes ("magistrates") whose duties included the absolute choice and election of the king of the realm.

1st Questions

- The 1st question of the New Testament:

  "Where is he that is born King of the Jews?"

- The 1st question of the Old Testament:

  God called to Adam "Where art thou?"
  Gen 3:9

- The first question in the Old Testament deals with the first Adam;
  the first question in the New Testament deals with the last Adam. 1 Cor 15:45

"Star" of Bethlehem?

- Balaam's prophecy?
  - *not* quoted by Matthew: Num 24:17
    Conjunctions? Isa 60:3
  - Kepler suggested the conjunction of Jupiter and Saturn in the constellation of Pisces in 7 B.C.
    - from an erroneous inference from *Josephus*. (Wrong date: 2 B.C.—4 B.C.)
- Not a "natural" phenomenon: it settled over a specific location…

Shekhinah?

- The Creation Gen 1
- The Abrahamic Covenant Gen 15
- Burning Bush Ex 3
- Pillar of fire by night Ex 13
- Flames at Pentecost Acts 2
- *Why not here?*

Pattern is Prophetic

- Exodus 4:22: Israel nationally spoken of as God's son Jer 31:9; Rom 9:4-5

All through Isaiah, the thought shifts between the nation and the Messiah:

- Isaiah 41:8
  Abraham as the friend of God, and Israel spoken of as if the nation was an individual, here Israel my servant
- Isaiah 42:1-4
  "spirit upon him," subject changed, no longer referring to nation, but now the Messiah
- Isaiah 52:13 - through 53
  The Jews interpret this chapter nationally, not individually

The Branch

צֶמַח *tsemach*

- "The Branch of the Lord" Isa 4:2
- Royal King from line of David Jer 23:5
- (Repeat of above) Jer 33:15
- Servant of Jehovah Zech 3:8
- Will build the Temple Zech 6:12
- Of 20 Hebrew words translated "branch," only on of them—*Tsemach*—is used exclusively of the Messiah

The Mazzaroth

- All the stars have a name Ps 147:4 Isa 40:26
- Zodiac: Ζωδιακος, from *Sodi*, "the Way"
- The Temple of Denderah, 2000 BC

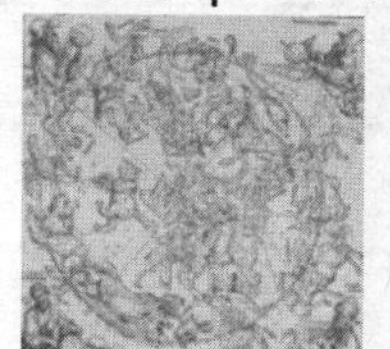

Virgo, the Virgin

Alpha: *Spica* (ear of corn).

Hebrew:	*Tsemach* (branch).
Arabic:	*Al Zimach* (branch).
Egypt:	*Aspolia* (the seed)

The Seed of the Woman
Gen 3:15
a *branch* in her right hand, ears of *corn* in her left.
John 12:21-24

Virgo is associated with the tribe of Zebulon, where Nazareth is located.

Shiloh

 שִׁילֹה *Shiloh:* he whose it is
"The scepter will not depart from Judah until He comes to whom it belongs."

- The term "*Shiloh*" was understood by the early rabbis and Talmudic authorities as referring to the Messiah.

  Targum Onkelos
  Targum Jonathan
  Targum Yerusahlmi

Sceptre Departs

- Herod the Great died
  - Herod Antipater: had been murdered
  - Herod Archelaus

    Appointed "Entharch" by Caesar Augustus
    Broadly rejected: Dethroned, Banished (6-7 AD)
    Josephus, *Antiqities*, 17:13
- Caponius appointed Procurator
  - The legal power of the Sanhedrin was immediately restricted and the adjudication of capital cases was lost. This was normal Roman policy. Josephus, *Wars of the Jews,* 2:8

Major Lessons

- The Messianic Line
  - The Truth is in the details
  - The Precision of God-breathed text
- Hermeneutics
  - Pattern as Prophecy

Matthew- SESSION 2: Chapter 2

1) Who were the Magi? How does the title "Rab-Mag" of Daniel explain the lion's den incident? What does this have to do with the events surrounding the birth of Christ?

2) Why was "Jerusalem troubled" by Magi's arrival?

3) Was the "Star of Bethlehem" an astronomical object? How do we know?

4) Of the three gifts presented to Christ at His birth, which will not be presented to Him in the Millennium? Why?

5) What were the principal hermeneutical lessons in this session?

Preparation for the Next Session:

Read Matthew Chapters 3 and 4; and John Chapter 1.

Group Discussion Questions: See the *Small Group Leaders* section of this workbook

Session 3

The Gospel of

Matthew

Chapters 3 & 4

Outline

- Chapter 1
  - Genealogy of Christ
  - Birth of Christ
- Chapter 2
  - The Visit of the Magi
- Chapter 3
  - John the Baptist
- Chapter 4
  - The Temptation of Christ

Chronology

- Tiberius appointed: 14 AD
  - Augustus died August 19, 14 AD
- (Within the) 15th year of Tiberius Luke 3:1
- Thus, ministry began in fall 28 AD
- 4th Passover: April 6, 32 AD

Sir Robert Anderson

- (Other chronologies assume a Friday crucifixion)

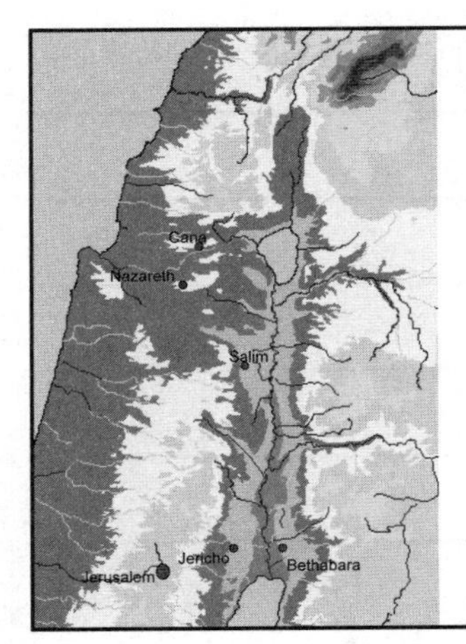

Autumn 28 AD

Begins at Nazareth

Baptism	John 1:28; Matt 3:13-17; Mark 1:9-11
Temptation	Matt 4:1-11; Luke 4:1-13
Salim	John 3:23

Cana: Nathaniel's home town
First disciples: John, Andrew, Peter, Philip, Nathaniel John 1:13-51

There was a man sent from God, whose name was John.
The same came for a witness, to bear witness of the Light, that all men through him might believe.
He was not that Light, but was sent to bear witness of that Light.
That was the true Light, which lighteth every man that cometh into the world. **John 1:6-9**

3 Anticipated

- Judaism is expecting 3 different people:
  - The Messiah (in a generic sense),
  - Elijah (prophesied to return) Mal 4:5,6
  - The Prophet of Moses: "that prophet" Deut 18
  - John denies being any of the three expected
- Mt 17 shows that Elijah and Moses have a peculiar role beyond their earthly ministry
  - The Two Witnesses? Rev 11

Shoes

- Moses and the burning bush, told to take off his shoes
- Tabernacle covered in badger/porpoise skins, which is what they were shoed with during the 40 years in the wilderness (that never wore out!)
- Boaz redeems the land to Naomi and takes a Gentile bride to wife;
  - the symbol of the contract is a shoe;
- John comments of the Messiah, "his shoes I'm not worthy to unloose..."

Baptism

- Why did Jesus insist upon being baptized? Did Jesus have any sins to confess?
  - He was sinless 2 Cor 5:21; 1 Pet 2:22; 1 John 3:5; John 14:3; Isa 53:12
- At John's baptism, Jesus is declaring publicly His *identity with* the sinner.
- This is His formal opening for His ministry: This event is commemorated by the trinity:
  - The Father, through the voice;
  - The Holy Spirit , descending dove-like;
  - The Son being baptized.

The Lamb of God

• Lamb of God	John 1:29
• Abel	Gen 4
• Isaac	Gen 22
• Offered: Passover	Ex 12
• Person	Isa 53
• Kinsman-Redeemer	Rev 5
• Glorified	Rev 22:1

Chapter 4

The Temptation of Christ

Satan

- Satan, as a person, a knowledgeable, malevolent, powerful ruler.
- A personal Satan, your adversary.
- Two errors about Satan:
  - We pretend he doesn't exist or
  - We become so conscious of him that he receives more credit than he deserves.
- He is a created being
  - He is not omnipresent; he has location
  - He is a dignity, real, powerful, yet defeated.

Our Refuge: His Word

- In all three responses, Jesus counters by quoting the Scriptures: "it is written"
  - Incidentally, all responses were from the book of Deuteronomy.
- Quoted from Deut 8:3. Forty years in the wilderness was for testing.
- One of the seven "I am" statements in John is "I am the Bread of Life," which is linked to manna from the wilderness.
  - "Thy words are found and I did eat them."

Ps 119; Jer 15:16 and John in Rev 10:9

The Ownership of Nations

- "The god of this world" is a title of Satan.
- Daniel 10 vs Gen 12
  - The destiny of America?
- Our heritage:
  - David Barton: Wallbuilders, et al
  - Election rhetoric today?
  - Character vs Destiny?

Isaiah's Prophecies

- Quoting from Isa 9:1,2 (LXX)
  Alluding to blessing and prophecies:
  - Zebulun Gen 49:13
  - Naphtali Gen 49:21
- Matthew is pointing out that prophecies of those two tribes are being fulfilled in the fact that the Messiah of Israel is present in their borders and is beginning to preach.

From that time Jesus began to preach, and to say, Repent: for the kingdom of heaven is at hand.

And Jesus, walking by the sea of Galilee, saw two brethren, Simon called Peter, and Andrew his brother, casting a net into the sea: for they were fishers.

And he saith unto them, Follow me, and I will make you fishers of men.

And they straightway left their nets, and followed him.

Matthew 4:17-20

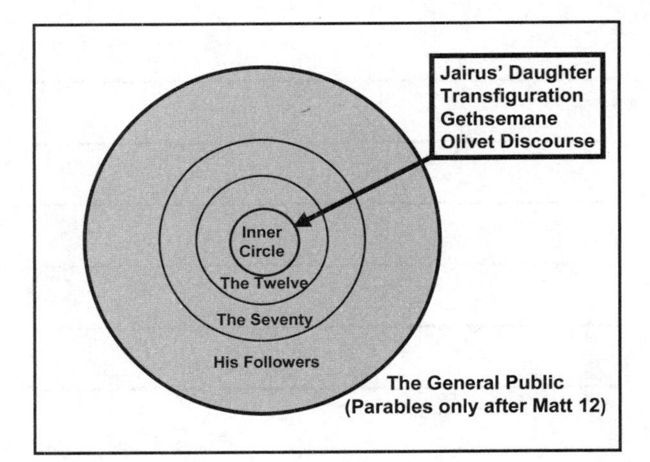

"The Sons of Thunder"

- John and his brother were nicknamed "Sons of Thunder" - they were fisherman, very strong people.
- These four are singled out by Matthew as an inner circle, often even narrowed down to three: Peter, James and John
  - There are number of occasions which only these three are allowed to experience Matt 17
- The four disciples are given a private briefing on the 2nd Coming: the Olivet Discourse. Matt 24-25

Major Lessons

- John the Baptist:
  - No one greater? (Mystery of Matt 11)
- The "Lamb of God"?
  - The Two Messiah view
- Temptations and their principal source
  - The ownership of the nation(s)
- The cost of discipleship
  - Leaving as well as cleaving

Matthew- SESSION 3: Chapters 3 & 4

1) What was the closing event of the Old Testament period? (Give references) On what Scripture is the "New Testament" based?

2) Who were the three venerates being anticipated by the Jewish leadership? On what basis? Which of these did John the Baptist fulfill?

3) Why was Jesus baptized?

4) What lessons can be drawn from the temptations of Christ?
What were Satan's stratagems challenging God's program?
What does Daniel 10 imply regarding this session?
What were the remedies against his stratagems?
What are the *prophetic* implications from this session?

5) In what ways are we commanded to "test" God?

6) What lessons can be inferred from the call of the disciples?

Preparation for the Next Session:

Study carefully Matthew 5, 6, and 7. Summarize the lessons given.

Group Discussion Questions: See the *Small Group Leaders* section of this workbook.

Session 4

The Gospel of

Matthew

Chapters 5, 6, 7
The "Sermon on the Mount"

The Beatitudes

- "Poor in spirit" v.3
  - Our attitude toward ourselves in which we feel our need and admit it
- "Mourn" v.4
  - Our attitude toward sin, a true sorrow for sin
- "Meek" v.5
  - Our attitude toward others; we are teachable; we do not defend ourselves when we are wrong
- "Hunger and thirst" v.6
  - Here our attitude toward God is expressed; we receive His righteousness by faith because we ask for it.

Beatitudes

- "Merciful" v.7
  - We have a forgiving spirit and love others
- "Pure in heart" v.8
  - We keep our lives and motives clean; holiness is happiness to us: no substitutes
- "Peacemakers" v 9
  - We should bring peace, between people and God, and between those who are at odds with each other
- "Persecuted" v.10
  - All who live godly lives will suffer persecution

"Poor in spirit"

- We must be empty before we can be full. The opposite of this is self-sufficiency. Our sufficiency is not of ourselves 2 Cor. 3:5
- The world promotes self-sufficiency, yet God dwells with the person whose heart is broken Isa. 57:15
- This does not mean false humility or cowardice; it means a proper attitude toward self, realizing how weak and sinful we are apart from Christ.
- Compare the two men Luke 18:9f

"Mourn"

- This is sincere sorrow for sin; our sin and the sins of others.
- How careless we are about sin! We excuse it, yet God hates it, and sin breaks God's heart.
- Beware of the sorrow of this world 2 Cor. 7:8–10
  - Peter mourned with godly sorrow and was forgiven;
  - Judas had remorse—the sorrow of this world—and he took his life.
- Micah is an example of those who mourn and are comforted Micah 7

"Meek"

- Meekness is not weakness!
- Jesus was meek Matt 11:29
  - yet He drove the changers from the temple.
- Moses was meek Num 12:3
  - yet he judged sinners; even faced Aaron with his sin.
- Meekness means not asserting my own rights, but living for the glory of God.
- Christians are to show meekness Eph 4:1–2; Titus 3:2
- So good that you have nothing to prove Ps 37

"Hunger and thirst"

- A true Christian has an appetite for spiritual things.
- Ask people what they desire and you will know what they are like.
- Character is what you are when no one is looking.
- This is evidence of your new life in Christ. How do you know if you're saved?
  - One way you can tell is by checking your appetites; what do you hunger and thirst after?
- The natural man will have nothing of this

"Merciful"

- Not legalism, but merely the working of the Biblical principle of sowing and reaping
- If we show mercy, because Christ has been merciful to us, then mercy will come back to us. Luke 16:1–13; James 2:13; Prov. 11:17
- We cannot earn mercy, but we must have hearts prepared to receive it.

"Pure in heart"

- Not sinlessness but the truth within. Ps. 51:6; 1 John 1:8
- It means a single heart, not divided between God and the world.
- No honest man can say that his heart is pure. How can the heart of man, which is desperately wicked, be made clean?
  - The Lord Jesus said, "Now ye are clean through the word which I have spoken unto you." John 15:3
  - It is by the washing of regeneration that we are made clean. Only the blood of Christ can cleanse us from all sin. Cf. John 1:7

"Peacemakers"

- This world is at war. Titus 3:3
- Christians have the Gospel of peace on their feet, so that wherever they go, they bring peace. Eph. 6:15
- This is not "peace at any price," for holiness is more important than a peace based on sin. James 3:17; Heb. 12:14
- Compromise is not peace; but Christians should not be contentious as they contend for the faith.

"Persecuted"

- We should be accused "falsely." We should never be guilty of deliberately inviting persecution. 2 Tim. 3:12
- If we live godly lives, suffering will come!
  - Note the rewards: we are in the same company as Christ and the prophets, and we shall be rewarded in heaven.

Salt

- Salt was used as a preservative; it preserves materials from corruption.
- Salt also creates thirst, and introduces flavor.
- Salt speaks of inward character that influences a decaying world. Our task is to keep our lives pure that we might "salt" this earth and hold back corruption so that the Gospel can get out.

Light

- Light speaks of the outward testimony of good works that points to God.
- Our good works must accompany our dedicated lives as we let our lights shine.

Pharisaical Error

- The scribes and Pharisees were not insincere; they tried to adhere to the keeping of the Law. Although misguided, they were zealous and sincere.
  - Anyone that tries to reconcile himself to God by his works, his rules, his legalism, is pharisaical.
- Is there any other way to heaven other than by Jesus Christ?
  - If there is, Jesus Christ's prayers were not answered In Gethsemane: Jesus pleaded with the Father 3 times for an alternative.

Righteousness

- Does the Christian need to "keep the Law?"
- The fact of the matter is that the Law is still a standard: It reveals to me that I cannot measure up to God's standard.
- This drives me to the cross of Christ.
  - The only way I can fulfill the Law is by accepting the only One who could fulfill it—Jesus Christ.

John 14:6

I am the way, the truth, & the light - no one comes to the Father except through me.

Jesus fulfilled the Law

1. Jesus became our sacrifice and shed His own sinless blood on our behalf. He offered Himself once for all for the sins of all mankind

   Hebrews 7:27, 9:12, 26, 28, 10:10, 1 Peter 3:18

   - Everything was fulfilled just before Jesus' death on the cross when He uttered His last words: "It is finished!" John 19:30

   tete,lestai = "Paid in full"

Jesus fulfilled the Law

2. The second way He fulfilled the law is that He taught and commanded what God's will is under the New Covenant for those who would enter the Kingdom of God.

- He gave a new set of rules to us. Paul called those rules Christ's law.
  - Some of those were the same as God gave in the Old Testament law.
  - Many were changed, but most of Old Testament law was *not* included at all in Christ's law.

613 laws in Christ's law

Gal. 5:18

The Purpose of the Law

- "Through the law we become conscious of sin." Rom 3:20
- "The law was added so that the trespass might increase." Rom 5:20
- sin become more evident
- "It was added because of transgressions until the Seed [the Lord Jesus Christ] to whom the promise referred had come." Gal 3:19
- "So the law was put in charge to lead us to Christ that we might be justified by faith." Gal 3:24
- "Now that faith has come, we are no longer under the supervision of the law." Gal 3:25

Matthew- SESSION 4: Chapter 5

1) What does the Sermon on the Mount have to do with the Gospel?

____

____

____

____

____

2) Match Column A with selections from Columns B and C:

Column A	[B]	[C]
1. "Poor in spirit"	[___]	[___]
2. "Mourn"	[___]	[___]
3. "Meek"	[___]	[___]
4. "Hunger and thirst"	[___]	[___]
5. "Merciful"	[___]	[___]
6. "Pure in heart"	[___]	[___]
7. "Peacemakers"	[___]	[___]
8. "Persecuted"	[___]	[___]

Column B

A. A true sorrow for sin.
B. Clean motives.
C. Attitude toward ourselves in which we feel our need and admit it.
D. Attitude toward others; not defending ourselves when we are wrong.
E. *Lex Talionis*
F. A forgiving spirit
G. Hardships with a purpose
H. Repairing relationships vertically and horizontally
I. Attitude toward God.

Column C

A. "Kingdom of Heaven"
B. "be filled"
C. "inherit the earth"
D. "be comforted"
E. "obtain mercy"
F. "shall see God"
G. "called the children of God"
H. "really cool dudes"

3) What are "jots and tittles"? How are they relevant?

4) Summarize the differences between the Law of Moses and the Law of Christ.

5) Should Christians fast? Why?

Preparation for the Next Session:

Read Matthew 6 & 7.

Group Discussion Questions: See the *Small Group Leaders* section of this workbook.

Session 5

The Manifesto of Our King

Matthew 5, 6, 7
The "Sermon on the Mount"
Part 2

Pharisees

- Separatists (Heb. *persahin*, from *parash*, "to separate")
- They were the successors of the Assideans (i.e., the "pious"), a party that originated in the time of Antiochus Epiphanes in revolt against his heathenizing policy.
- The first mention of them is in a description by Josephus of the three sects or schools into which the Jews were divided (B.C. 145).
  - The other two sects were the Essenes and the Sadducees.

Sadducees

- They were probably the outcome of the influence of Grecian customs and philosophy during the period of Greek domination.
- The first time they are met with is in connection with John the Baptist's ministry. They came out to him when on the banks of the Jordan, and he said to them:

  "O generation of vipers, who hath warned you to flee from the wrath to come?" Mt 3:7

Which "Commandments"?

- What are "these commandments" being referred to?
  - *The ones we find in the remainder of Matthew 5 and continuing in chapters 6 and 7.*
  - Jesus will emphasize "my words" Cf. Matt 7:24-27
  - His call to *obedience* John 14:15, 21, 23; 1 John 5:3

The Purpose of the Law

- "Through the law we become conscious of sin." Rom 3:20
- "The law was added so that the trespass might increase." Rom 5:20
- "It was added because of transgressions until the Seed [the Lord Jesus Christ] to whom the promise referred had come." Gal 3:19
- "So the law was put in charge to lead us to Christ that we might be justified by faith." Gal 3:24
- "Now that faith has come, we are no longer under the supervision of the law." Gal 3:25

Levit. 19:18

Religious Practice

- Chapter 5 the King speaks of the righteousness which His subjects must *possess.*
  - It must be a righteousness to exceed the righteousness of the scribes and Pharisees, and that comes only through trust in Christ.
- Chapter 6 deals with the external part of religion: the righteousness that the subjects of the kingdom are to *practice.*
  - The internal motive, of course, is the important thing in what you do for God.

Matthew 6

"Disciples Prayer"

- Jesus couldn't really pray this prayer; it was only a model for the disciples.
- There is no further mention of it in the Book of Acts or any of the epistles.
- For the *real* Lord's Prayer, a study in intimacy with the Father, see John 17.

The Lord's (Own) Prayer

- The Lord could not pray the model He gave His disciples.

John 17 details the true Lord's prayer

- His relationship
- His commitment—and the Father's—to us
- (He prays for His own, *not* for the world)

John 17:9

"Be not anxious"

- Worry is a sin. It is a form of blasphemy.
- Worry is assuming a responsibility that God did not intend for you to have.
- *Worry is a trickle of fear that soon cuts a crevice so deep it drains all other thoughts away…*

Planning?

- Planning: Futurity of today's decisions
  Peter Drucker
- The need for forecasting
  - Stewardship requirements 1 Cor 4:2
  - Counting the cost Luke 14:28
- Non-linearities
  Plan; but don't depend
- Darwin Award candidates

Matthew 7

- Whole passage is to believers
  Cf. Rom 14:4-13, 1 Cor 4:5
- There are occasions we are to judge within the fellowship. Cf. 1 Cor 5
- We are not to judge the intent of the heart; we are to be fruit inspectors.
- Scripture does not say that you cannot go to law against a brother; there are some procedures we should invoke first.
  Mt 18:15

The Golden Rule

- Confused with K'ung Fu-Tze, a writer in China, also known as Confucius:
  - He says don't do that which you don't want people to do to you. *It's negative and it's passive.*
  - Same idea also found in the Talmud, again in the negative, don't do that to somebody else that which you don't want him or her to do to you.

The Golden Rule

- "Therefore" implies a linkage to the previous verse
  - What Jesus is expressing is *not* just an ethical principle: He is linking this practice with a supernatural agency of the Father.
- The Golden Rule does not include the gospel: it is the fruit of the gospel.
- The concept of the Golden rule as described by Confucius or the Talmud, is not a declaration of God's love: this is.
  - *It is positive, and an active imperative*

Personal Jeopardy

- There are supernatural spirits that will attempt to seduce you. 1 Tim 4:1
- You can be derailed by pseudo-intellectualism, the prattling of science or knowledge falsely so-called. Col 2:8 1 Tim 6:20
- Does our Shepherd lose His sheep? *Not this shepherd!* John 10:27-30

"The Principle of Expositional Constancy"

- The theory that an idiom is used the same way throughout Scripture:
  - "Rock": Exodus, Numbers: the rock is Jesus Christ 1 Cor 10:4
  - Stone
    - Builders rejected Ps 118:22;Isa 8:14; Mat 21:42,44; Acts 4:11;2 Pet 2:6-8;
    - Headstone of the corner Gen 49:24; Isa 28:16; Dan 2:34,35; Mark 12:10; Luk 20:17; Eph 2:20
  - Sure foundation Isa 28:16; Rom 9:33

In Conclusion

- Who is speaking: the Ruler of Reality.
- Where are we headed?

  ...In this interval between the
  Miracle of our Origin and the
  Mystery of our destiny...

  ...Pilgrims in a simulated universe

  ...Heading outside our time domain
- Are we serious about Him?

MATTHEW- SESSION 5: Chapters 6 & 7

1) Summarize the primary lesson of the Epistle to the Galatians.

2) Explain how a "debt to society" was accounted for in the Roman period. How did this liability impact a jailer? Explain the meaning of ***tetelestai*** ("it is finished").

3) Summarize the attributes of "sincerity" and "simplicity" with respect to prayer, with examples.

4) List the reasons that the "Lord's Prayer" as given in the Sermon on the Mount *does not* apply to Jesus Christ.

5) What is the primary point of the "Unrighteous Steward" in Luke 16?

6) In what ways is "worry" an inappropriate condition for the Christian?

7) Contrast the Golden Rule in its active and passive aspects.

8) How can one be sure of their position in regards to Matthew 7:21-23?

9) What is "the Principle of Expositional Constancy"? Give examples.

10) Explain the distinctions between the Law of Moses and the Law of Christ.

Preparation for the Next Session:

Read Matthew Chapters 8 & 9.

Group Discussion Questions: See the *Small Group Leaders* section of this workbook.

Session 6

The Gospel of

Matthew

Chapter 8 & 9

Outline

Section II

8	Calming the Storm
	Demoniac at Gadara
9	Call of Matthew
	Jairus' Daughter
	Woman with issue of blood
10	The 12 sent out
11	John the Baptist: response
12	Sabbath issues
	The Unpardonable Sin

Chapter 8

Healings

Calming the Storm

The Demoniac at Gadara

Leprosy

- In the Bible there appears no cure for leprosy other than the Lord Himself.
  - Miriam — Num 12:13
  - Naaman — 2 Kgs 5:1-15
- Dapsone is a drug that treats it.
  - The resistance to that drug is increasing
  - 2 million known cases; suspect about 11 million if all were known

Luke's Role?

- Luke also talks a lot about Centurions.
  - Luke is always very kind to Centurions **Luke 7:4**
- When Paul invoked his Roman citizenship and appealed to Rome **Acts 25:11**
  - The Roman law required that written documentation of the appealed case had to precede the hearing
- It is believed by some scholars that Luke I & 2 (Gospel and Acts) were those required documents
  - Luke seems preoccupied to demonstrate that all the insurrections and public unrest were always the response of Judaism (by the Jews, not by Gentiles)
  - Roman officials were "good guys" in Luke's narratives.

"Jesus Boat"

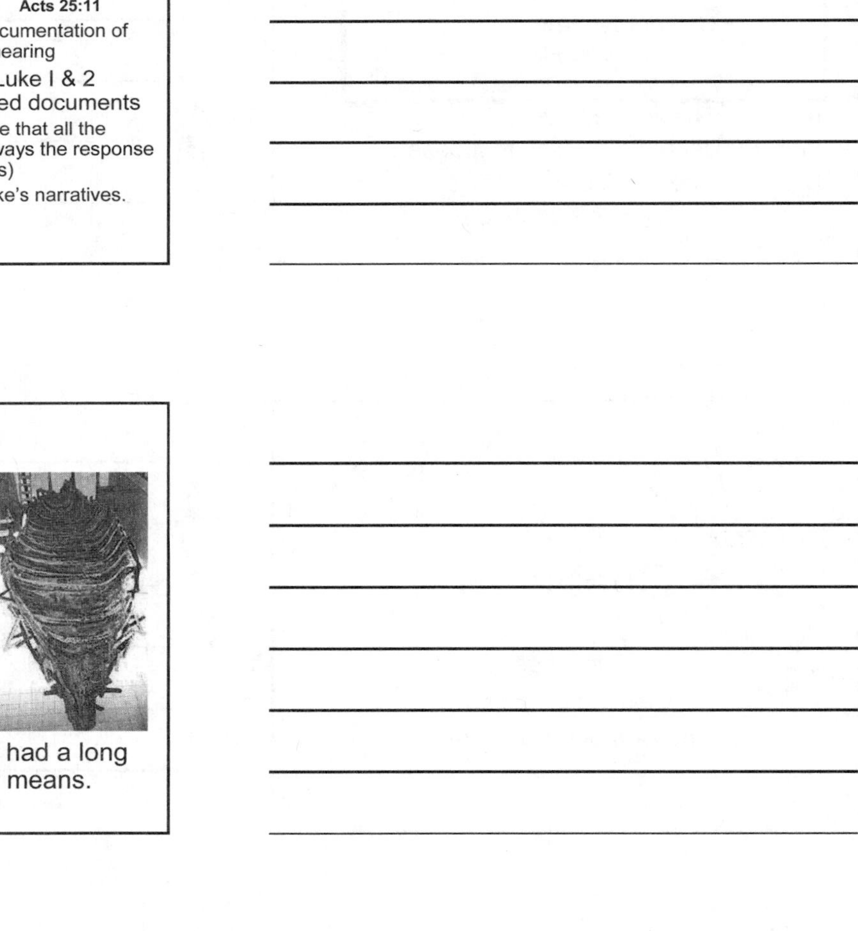

- 26 1/2 feet long, 7 1/2 feet wide and 4 1/2 feet high.
- Dated between 100 B.C. and 100 A.D.
- Numerous repairs, the reuse of timbers and a multiplicity of wood types (twelve) evident in the hull, suggest that this vessel had a long work life by an owner of meager means.

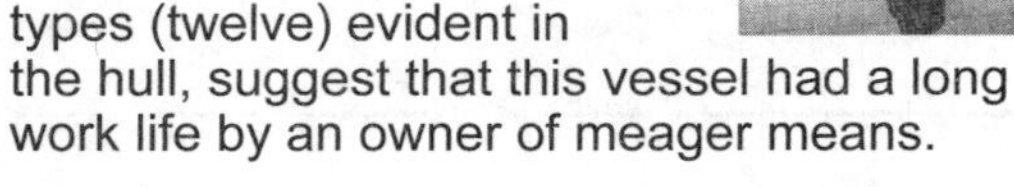

Declaration of Deity

- What they announced was not known at this time:
  - They recognized that there is a time coming that they would rather avoid.
  - They know that He is in control of it.
  - They are acknowledging His deity, and their destiny and His control of it.

Demonology

- Different than fallen angels
  - Disembodied Nephilim?
  - Rephaim?
- Dan 10?
- **Demons**
  - We know that demons are at Satan's control, they are some of his resources, they are malevolent, they are dangerous, they are around, and if you are not a Christian you are vulnerable to them.
- Not simply a psychiatric disorder.
- They could not indwell animals without permission.

Matthew 9

Healings
Call of Matthew
Jairus' Daughter
Woman with issue of blood

The Call of Matthew

- The call of Levi was the culmination of the previous two miracles:
  - The cleansing of the leper
  - The man taken with palsy
- Jesus had demonstrated His authority:
  - to make a person ceremonially clean
  - to forgive sins
- Now those two authorities were brought to bear on one who was to become His disciple.

A Tax Collector

- He was sitting at the place of toll, the customs house **Matt 9:9**
- The Romans collected taxes through a franchise system called "tax farming":
  - They assessed a fixed tax figure and then sold the right to collect them to the highest bidder. The buyer then had to hand over the assessed figure at the end of the year and could keep any excess.
  - This invited extortion.

Professional Stenographers

- By hand: "*manu*-scripts"
- Specifically named:
  - Romans 16:22 Tertius
  - 1 Corinthians 1:1 Sosthenes
  - 2 Corinthians 1:1 Timothy
  - Philippians 1:1 Timothy
  - Colossians 1:1 Timothy
  - 2 Thess 1:1 Silvanus
  - Philemon 1:1 Timothy
  - 1 Peter 5:12: Silvanus

The Marriage Fulfilled

- Covenant established: 1 Cor 11:25
- Purchase price: 1 Cor 6:19-20
- Bride set apart: Eph 5:25-27; 1 Cor 1:2; 6:11; Heb 10:10; 13:12
- Reminded of the covenant: 1 Cor 11:25-26
- Bridegroom left for the Father's house…
- Returns by surprise to gather His Bride 1 Thes 4:16-17

Hems

- In ancient Mesopotamia, "to cut off the hem" was to strip one of his personality, authority, etc.
- A husband could divorce his wife by cutting off the hem of her robe.
- A nobleman would authenticate his name on a clay tablet by pressing the hem on the soft clay.

Hems

- Fringes on Levitical garments Num 15:38, 39; Deut 22:12; Ex 28:33,34
- God's Covenant with Israel: "I spread my (*shuwl*) over thee.." Ezek 16:8; Ex 39:25,26
- Joseph's coat: Brothers were envious Gen 37:3-4
- The Lord's hem sought for healing Mt 14:36; Mk 6:56
- Goal of the woman with the issue of blood Mt 9:20-21; Mk 5:31
- Ruth & Boaz: "Spread thy (*shuwl*) over thine handmaid..." Ruth 3:9
  - she was thereby requesting him to exercise his authority over her

The Issue of Blood

- Makes one ceremonially unclean; anything touched was ceremonially unclean. Lev 15:19-33; 18:19; 20:18
- She was a *Gentile*; otherwise she would not be allowed there in the crowd.

Pattern is Prophecy

- Is there a symbolic connection?
  - She has had the issue of blood for 12 years
  - The daughter raised from the dead was 12 years old.
- Who is Jesus Christ *called on* to raise?
  - A Daughter of Zion Zech 9:9
    18x in the book of Lamentations alone; that is a title of Israel.
  - En route to raising the daughter of Zion, a Gentile woman is healed…

Christ's Credentials

- Power over Disease 8:1–17
  - Leprosy vv. 1–4
  - Palsy vv. 5–13
  - Fever vv. 14–17
- Power over Nature 8:18–27
- Power over Satan 8:28–34
- Power over Sin 9:1–17
- Power over Death 9:18–26
- Power over Darkness 9:27–31
- Power over Demons 9:32–38

MATTHEW- SESSION 6: Chapters 8 & 9

1) What is leprosy, as a disease? What is leprosy as a Biblical type? Why?

2) Why did Jesus require the healed leper to show it to the priest?

3) Why do some scholars believe that Luke's writings (both volumes) were Roman legally required documents?

4) Explain Matthew 8:12.

5) List the insights we can gather from the encounter with the demoniac at Gadara. How many demons were involved?

6) Contrast the differences between fallen angels and the demons revealed in the New Testament.

7) Why did the woman with an issue of blood target the hem of Jesus' garment? Why do we suspect that she was a ***gentile?***

8) In what way is Jesus a "bridegroom"? How are the ancient Jewish wedding traditions a prophetic type? What is the next event to be expected?

Preparation for the Next Session:

Read Matthew chapters 10 and 11: Review the instructions to the disciples; How do they apply to us today?
Review John 1: In what way is "the least in the Kingdom of Heaven greater than John (the Baptist)"?

Group Discussion Questions: See the *Small Group Leaders* section of this workbook.

Session 7

The Gospel of

Matthew

Chapter 10 & 11

Outline

Section II

8	Calming the Storm
	Demoniac at Gadara
9	Call of Matthew
	Jairus' Daughter
	Woman with issue of blood
10	The 12 sent out
11	Response to John the Baptist
12	Sabbath issues
	The Unpardonable Sin

Chapter 10

Matthias or Paul?

- Some view Paul as the 12th as the replacement for Judas (vs. than Matthias).
- The apostles' mission was very Jewish.
- Matthias was chosen to be the 12th apostle after Judas had betrayed Jesus.
- Paul was the apostle to the Gentiles. Paul mentions the twelve, and Matthias at that point was one of the twelve. 1 Cor 15:5

Instructions

- This chapter gives instructions to
  - The apostles in the past vv. 1–15
  - The apostles of the future Tribulation period vv. 16–23
  - God's servants today vv. 24–42

Two Commissions

- The Kingdom presentation is withdrawn when Israel rejects it. Chapter 12
- Then the focus will shift to the Gentiles, the Crucifixion and the Resurrection, and a new commission will be given for the *eccelsia*, the Church.
- When this one is completed, the Church will be taken out and the first commission resumed (by the 144,000).
- The New Commission:
  Mt 28:19, 20; Mk 16:15; Lk 24:46;47; Acts 1:8. Cf. Acts 2:23. Also, Isa 60:1-16.

Chapter 11

Say to them that are of a fearful heart, Be strong, fear not: behold, your God will come with vengeance, even God with a recompense; he will come and save you.
Then the eyes of the blind shall be opened, and the ears of the deaf shall be unstopped.
Then shall the lame man leap as an hart, and the tongue of the dumb sing: for in the wilderness shall waters break out, and streams in the desert.

Isaiah 35:4-6

Elijah Promised

- John was the last of the OT prophets.
- Christ states that John's ministry was the fulfillment of Malachi 3:1.
  - Had the nation received Jesus, John would have been the Elijah promised by God. v. 14, Cf. 17:10–13
  - Because they rejected both John and Jesus, the literal and final fulfillment will not come until the end times. Malachi 3:1–3

And his disciples asked him, saying, Why then say the scribes that Elias must first come?

And Jesus answered and said unto them, Elias truly shall first come, and restore all things.

But I say unto you, That Elias is come already, and they knew him not, but have done unto him whatsoever they listed. Likewise shall also the Son of man suffer of them.

Then the disciples understood that he spake unto them of John the Baptist

Matthew 17:10-13

For John came neither eating nor drinking, and they say, He hath a devil.

The Son of man came eating and drinking, and they say, Behold a man gluttonous, and a winebibber, a friend of publicans and sinners. But wisdom is justified of her children.

Matthew 11:18,19

Then began he to upbraid the cities wherein most of his mighty works were done, because they repented not:

Woe unto thee, Chorazin! woe unto thee, Bethsaida! for if the mighty works, which were done in you, had been done in Tyre and Sidon, they would have repented long ago in sackcloth and ashes.

But I say unto you, It shall be more tolerable for Tyre and Sidon at the day of judgment, than for you.

Matthew 11:20-22

And thou, Capernaum, which art exalted unto heaven, shalt be brought down to hell: for if the mighty works, which have been done in thee, had been done in Sodom, it would have remained until this day.

But I say unto you, That it shall be more tolerable for the land of Sodom in the day of judgment, than for thee.

Matthew 11:23,24

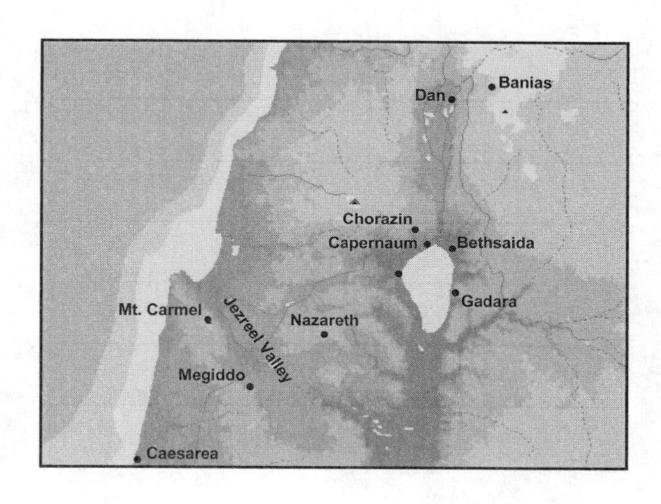

At that time Jesus answered and said, I thank thee, O Father, Lord of heaven and earth, because thou hast hid these things from the wise and prudent, and hast revealed them unto babes.

Even so, Father: for so it seemed good in thy sight.

All things are delivered unto me of my Father: and no man knoweth the Son, but the Father; neither knoweth any man the Father, save the Son, and *he* to whomsoever the Son will reveal *him*.

Matthew 11:25-27

Come unto me, all ye that labour and are heavy laden, and I will give you rest.

Take my yoke upon you, and learn of me; for I am meek and lowly in heart: and ye shall find rest unto your souls.

For my yoke *is* easy, and my burden is light.

Matthew 11:28-30

Healings (Summary)

8	Leper
	Centurian's servant
	Peter's Mother-in-law
	Demoniacs at Gadara
9	Palsy
	Jairus' daughter
	Woman with issue of blood
	2 blind men
12	Withered hand
	Blind and dumb

- The Revelation of the King is now complete 1–10
- The Rebellion against the King begins to appear 11–13

In this section, the Jews rebel against every revelation Christ gave of Himself:

- He was announced by John
  - They allowed John to be arrested 11:1–19
- He performed many miracles
  - The cities refused to repent 11:20–30
- He announced His principles
  - They argued with Him about them 12:1–21
- He revealed His Person
  - They said He worked with Satan 12:22–50

MATTHEW- SESSION 7: Chapters 10 & 11

1) What is the difference between a "disciple" and an "apostle"?

2) Who was the replacement for Judas among "the twelve"? Who were the alternatives?

3) How do "Hades" and "Gehenna" compare? Contrast them.

4) Explain Matthew 10:34: "Think not that I am come to send peace on earth: I came not to send peace, but a sword." How does this compare with "Blessed are the peacemakers…"?

5) If John the Baptist was the "greatest born of a woman," how can "the least in the kingdom of heaven" be greater than John? Was John saved? Explain.

Preparation for the Next Session:

Read Matthew 12. Does a Christian need to observe the Sabbath? What is the "Unpardonable Sin"?

Group Discussion Questions: See the *Small Group Leaders* section of this workbook.

Session 8

The Gospel of

Matthew

Chapter 12

Outline

Section II

8	Calming the Storm
	Demoniac at Gadara
9	Call of Matthew
	Jairus' Daughter
	Woman with issue of blood
10	The 12 sent out
11	Response to John the Baptist
12	Sabbath issues
	The Unpardonable Sin

Chapter 12

- The end of an important section
- Chapter 12 ends the presentation of the kingdom to Israel.
  - The rejection of Jesus Christ did not begin at the cross, but in Chapter 12.
  - One will note that Jesus will "shift gears" dramatically after Chapter 12:
    - Seven Kingdom Parables in Chapter 13

David's Flight from Saul

- The ark itself rested at Kiriath Jearim after the capture of the ark in 1104 BC.
  1 Sam 7:2; 2 Sam. 6:3-4
- Currently it was at Nob, the "city of priests," halfway between Jerusalem and Gibeah, where David fled after he made his final break with Saul.
- The Tabernacle was a secure area for the priests only, from the tribe of Levi.
- David, although anointed King, was of the tribe of Judah.

So the priest gave him hallowed bread: for there was no bread there but the shewbread, that was taken from before the LORD, to put hot bread in the day when it was taken away.

1 Samuel 21:6

- David's eating illustrated a concession that the Law permitted:
  —life is more holy than bread

Sabbatical Conflicts

- Plucking grain on the Sabbath Matt 12:1-4; Mark 2:23-26; Luke 6:1-4
  - He also reminded His critics that the priests in the Temple worked on Sabbath Matt 12:5
  - He referred to circumcising a male on the Sabbath day Lev 12:3; John 7:22, 23
  - Jesus asserted His lordship over the Sabbath Matt 12:8; Mark 2:28; Luke 6:5
- The healing of the withered hand Matt 12:8-14; Mark 3:1-5
- The healing a woman who had a spirit of infirmity for 18 years Luke 13:10-17

Seven Healings on the Sabbath

1.	Demoniac, in Capernaum	Mk 1:21-27
2.	Peter's mother-in-law	Mk 1:29-31
3.	Impotent Man	Jn 5:1-9
4.	Man with withered hand	Mk 3:1-6; Mt 12:8-14
5.	Woman bowed together	Lk 13:10-17
6.	Man with Dropsy	Lk 14:1-6
7.	Man born blind	Jn 9:1-14

Not all healings were on the Sabbath: healing on Sunday: Mk 1:32

Some Basic Questions

- How many of each animal did Noah take into the Ark? Genesis 7
- On what days did they gather Manna? Exodus 16
- When was the Law given? Exodus 20
- For whom was the Sabbath made?

The sabbath was made for man, and not man for the sabbath: Mark 2:27

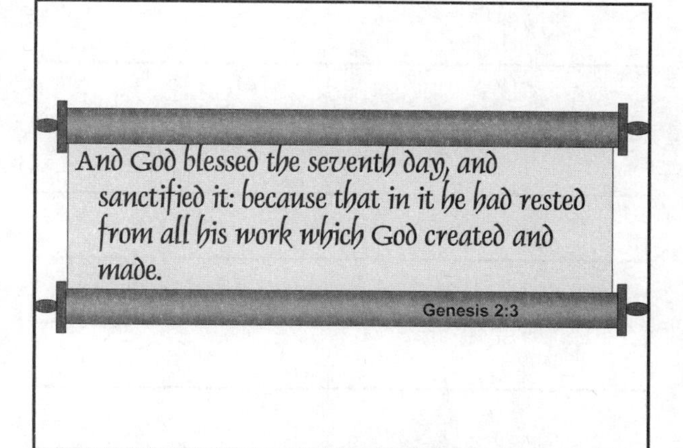

Two Extremes

There appear to be two potential pitfalls before us:

1. To ignore, and thus forfeit, a special opportunity for blessing;

   or the alternative hazard:

2. To deny the teachings of the Epistles of Romans, Galatians, Colossians, and Hebrews

The First or Seventh Day?

- The Resurrection took place on Sunday.
- Jesus appeared to His disciples on four Sunday occasions. Mt 28:1 Mk 16:2 Lk 24:1 Jn 20:1
- Pentecost, the birth of the church, was, by definition, on a Sunday. Acts 2:1
- They did meet on a Sunday night. Acts 20:7
- Some suggest the Ascension occurred on a Sunday:
  (With 40 days intervening between the Resurrection and the Ascension, this appears unlikely.) Acts 1:9

Apostolic Practice?

- While the argument is made that Sunday was their practice, it is less than clear
- The oft quoted 1 Cor 16:1, 2 is actually unclear:
  "....that there be no gatherings when I come."?
- The assertion that we never see Christ meeting with His disciples on any other day. appears to be contradicted by John 20:26:
  " .... after 8 days again....

Prophetic Implications

- Sabbaths will continue as a basis for worship in the Millennium. Isa 66:22, 23
- The gate to the inner court of the Millennial Temple will be opened only on the Sabbath and the day of the new moon. Ezek 46:1ff
- This would seem to refute a permanent substitution of Sunday for the Saturday *Sabbath.*

Sabbath Day Issues

- We need to realize that we are not saved by the days we keep, we are saved by the Lord we keep.
- The Sabbath is a time of devotion, not a subjection to rules; It is a benefit to be taken advantage of. Rom 14:5; Col 2:16
- Jesus Christ is the fulfillment of the Sabbath day for you and me. Heb 4

The Unpardonable Sin

- The ministry of the Holy Spirit is to convict you of sin, and your need for a savior, while Satan tries to condemn you for your sins.
- Remember Rom 8:1:
  - How does one tell if it is conviction from the Holy Spirit or condemnation from Satan?
  - Is what is happening drawing you closer to or away from God?
  - If your feeling of remorse for your sin is drawing you into God's Word, than that is the Holy Spirit.
  - If the feelings, attitudes, thoughts and doubts over the issue, cause you to shun the Word, that is Satan trying to get you on a guilt trip.

Hades, Sheol, Ghenna?

- Jesus is referring to the grave and Hades, in the center of the earth.
- Hades was temporary place.
  - Ghenna is in the outer darkness, permanent
- There is a gulf between the good part and bad part of Hades . Luke 16
  - (The Abusso was probably the center of Hades. The Abusso has no bottom and the only place on earth with no bottom is the center of the earth.)

Friday Crucifixion?

1. Sign of Jonah Matthew 12:40
2. "Sabbaths past" Matthew 28:1 (sabba,twn is plural: the Feast of Unleavened Bread as well as Shabbat intervened)
3. Trip from Jericho 6 days before Passover John 12:1

Turning Point…

- This is a major turning point in Matthew's Gospel.
- From this point on, Jesus will only speak to the public in parables.
- The reason may surprise you…

MATTHEW- SESSION 8: Chapter 12

1) In what way is Chapter 12 distinctive in the structure of Matthew's Gospel?

2) What was Jesus' point in alluding to David's intrusion into the priest's office and partaking of the showbread in 1 Samuel 15?

3) When was the Sabbath established? To whom does it apply today? Is its observance in Exodus 16 relevant today? On what days will the Millennial Temple be opened?

4) How many of each animal did Noah take into the ark? How did he know what was "clean" and "unclean"?

5) What are two pitfalls regarding the keeping of the Sabbath day?

6) Was the crucifixion on a Friday? What are the alternatives? How does it relate to Passover? When was the Lord's Supper?

7) Did Jesus have brothers and sisters? Explain.

Preparation for the Next Session:

Read Matthew 13. Review your notes on the Letters to the Seven Churches, Revelation 2 and 3.

Group Discussion Questions: See the *Small Group Leaders* section of this workbook.

Session 9

The Gospel of

Matthew

Chapter 13

A Major Turning Point:

The Kingdom Parables

Matthew 13

Matthew 13

3-9	1: Sower & 4 Soils
10-17	Why Parables?
18-23	Sower & 4 Soils Explained
24-30	2: Tares & Wheat
31-32	3: Mustard Seed
33	4: Woman & Leaven
34-35	Why Parables? (continued)
36-43	Tares & Wheat Explained
44	5: Treasure in the Field
45-46	6: Pearl of Great Price
46-50	7: Dragnet

Why Parables?

And the disciples came, and said unto him, Why speakest thou unto them in parables?

He answered and said unto them, Because it is given unto you to know the mysteries of the kingdom of heaven, but to them it is not given.

For whosoever hath, to him shall be given, and he shall have more abundance: but whosoever hath not, from him shall be taken away even that he hath.

Matthew 13:10-12

But of the times and the seasons, brethren, ye have no need that I write unto you.

For yourselves know perfectly that the day of the Lord so cometh as a thief in the night.

For when they shall say, Peace and safety; then sudden destruction cometh upon them, as travail upon a woman with child; and they shall not escape.

But ye, brethren, are not in darkness, that that day should overtake you as a thief.

1 Thessalonians 5:1-3

Ye are all the children of light, and the children of the day: we are not of the night, nor of darkness.

Therefore let us not sleep, as *do* others; but let us watch and be sober.

For they that sleep sleep in the night; and they that be drunken are drunken in the night.

But let us, who are of the day, be sober, putting on the breastplate of faith and love; and for an helmet, the hope of salvation.

For God hath not appointed us to wrath, but to obtain salvation by our Lord Jesus Christ.

1 Thessalonians 5:5-9

Hear, ye deaf; and look, ye blind, that ye may see.

Who *is* blind, but my servant? or deaf, as my messenger *that* I sent? who *is* blind as *he that is* perfect, and blind as the LORD'S servant?

Seeing many things, but thou observest not; opening the ears, but he heareth not.

Isaiah 42:18-20

And he said, Go, and tell this people, Hear ye indeed, but understand not; and see ye indeed, but perceive not.

Make the heart of this people fat, and make their ears heavy, and shut their eyes; lest they see with their eyes, and hear with their ears, and understand with their heart, and convert, and be healed.

Isaiah 6:9,10

Why Parables?

All these things spake Jesus unto the multitude in parables; and without a parable spake he not unto them:

That it might be fulfilled which was spoken by the prophet, saying, I will open my mouth in parables; I will utter things which have been kept secret from the foundation of the world.

Matthew 13:34,35

Hidden Secret?

Whereby, when ye read, ye may understand my knowledge in the mystery of Christ
Which in other ages was not made known unto the sons of men, as it is now revealed unto his holy apostles and prophets by the Spirit;
That the Gentiles should be fellow heirs, and of the same body, and partakers of his promise in Christ by the gospel:

Ephesians 3:4-6

Four Soils (Summary)

1. Wayside without understanding
   - Birds steal the seed away
2. Stony places without root
   - Fail under pressure
3. Among thorns
   - Too entangled in the cares of this world
4. Good ground
   - Hearing and understand: bear much fruit

Tares & Wheat: Explained

Then Jesus sent the multitude away, and went into the house: and his disciples came unto him, saying, Declare unto us the parable of the tares of the field.
He answered and said unto them, He that soweth the good seed is the Son of man;

Matthew 13:36,37

Tares & Wheat: Explained

The field is the world; the good seed are the children of the kingdom; but the tares are the children of the wicked one;

The enemy that sowed them is the devil; the harvest is the end of the world; and the reapers are the angels.

Matthew 13:38,39

Student Diligence:

Jesus saith unto them, Have ye understood all these things? They say unto him, Yea, Lord.

Then said he unto them, Therefore every scribe *which is* instructed unto the kingdom of heaven is like unto a man *that is* an householder, which bringeth forth out of his treasure *things* new and old.

Matthew 13:51,52

Prophetic Profile?

- Ephesus — The Apostolic Church
- Smyrna — The Persecuted Church
- Pergamos — The Married Church
- Thyatira — The Medieval Church
- Sardis — Denominational Church
- Philadelphia — Missionary Church
- Laodicea — Apostate Churc

The Seven Kingdom Parables

Rev. 2 & 3	Matthew 13
• Ephesus	• The Sower and 4 Soils
• Smyrna	• The Tares and the Wheat
• Pergamos	• The Mustard Seed
• Thyatira	• The Woman & the Leaven
• Sardis	• The Treasure in the Field
• Philadelphia	• The Pearl of Great Price
• Laodicea	• The Dragnet

Paul's Epistles

7 Churches	**Romans** 1, 2 Corinthians Galatians Ephesians Philippians Colossians 1, 2 Thessalonians
Pastors	1, 2 Timothy Titus Philemon

Seven Churches

Jesus:	Paul:
• Ephesus	• Ephesus
• Smyrna	• Philippians
• Pergamos	• Corinthians
• Thyatira	• Galatians
• Sardis	• Romans
• Philadelphia	• Thessalonians
• Laodicea	• Colossians

MATTHEW- SESSION 9: Chapter 13

1) Why did Jesus speak in parables?

2) What was unique about the contents of the parables in this chapter? What subject do they deal with which "was kept secret from the foundation of the world"?

3) List and explain the significance of each of the seven parables. What is the *personal* application of each?

4) What is the significance of the birds in the parables? How does this impact the parable of the Mustard Seed?

5) Oysters were not kosher; how does this impact our understanding of the Pearl of Great Price?

Preparation for the Next Session:

Read Matthew 14 & 15.

Group Discussion Questions: See the *Small Group Leaders* section of this workbook.

Session 10

The Gospel of

Matthew

Chapters 14 & 15

Seven Churches

Jesus:	Paul:
Ephesus	Ephesus
Smyrna	Philippians
Pergamos	Corinthians
Thyatira	Galatians
Sardis	Romans
Philadelphia	Thessalonians
Laodicea	Colossians

Herod the Great

- The son of Antipater, an Idumaean, and Cypros, an Arabian of noble descent.
  - B.C. 47 Julius Caesar made Antipater, a "wily Idumaean," procurator of Judea, who divided his territories between his four sons, Galilee falling to the lot of Herod.
- B.C. 40: Appointed tetrarch of Judea by Mark Antony and also king of Judea by the Roman senate.
- He was of a stern and cruel disposition. "He was brutish and a stranger to all humanity."

Salome(1)

- Wife of Zebedee; among the "women who followed Jesus from Galilee, ministering unto Him." Mt. 27:55,56; Cf. Mk 15:40
  - She requested for her two seats of honor on Christ's right hand and left in His kingdom and shared with her sons in His rebuke, but was not the less zealous in her attachment to Him. Mt. 20:20
  - She was at His crucifixion, "beholding afar off." Mk 15:40
  - She was at His sepulchre by early dawn. Mk 16:1
  - (Some infer her to be the Virgin Mary's sister).

Salome (2)

- Herodias' daughter by her former husband Herod Philip.
  Josephus Ant. 18:5, section 4; Mt. 14:6; Mk 6:22
- She danced before Herod Antipas, and at her mother's instigation, asked for John the Baptist's head.
- Salome married first Philip, tetrarch of Trachonitis, her paternal uncle, then Aristobulus, king of Chalcis.

Herod the Great

- After the death of Mariamne's sons (Antipater, 7 BC), Augustus is said to have exclaimed:
  - It would be better to be one of Herod's swine than Herod's sons,"
  - (A pun on the similar sounding Greek terms for swine and son, *hus*, *huios*).
  - Herod, as a professed Jew, his swine as unclean were safe from death, but his sons were not.

Herod the Great

- Antipater
- Aristobulus
- Alexander
- Herod Philip
- Herod Antipas
- Archelaus
- Herod Philip

John the Baptist's Ministry

- John had heralded the coming of the King and had faithfully preached God's truth.
  - Christ must increase, and he must decrease John 3:30
- Any Christian who is faithful to the Word of God, as John was, will suffer persecution.
  - The world is not the friend of the Christian.
  - The world rejected the King and will also reject His messengers.

The Herods

- Herod the Great
  - Slew the children in Bethlehem Matt 2:16–18
- Herod Antipas
  - Younger son of Herod the Great
  - Not really a king, but merely a tetrarch: (a ruler over a fourth of the kingdom)
  - Had John the Baptist killed and before whom Jesus was silent Luke 23:5–12
- Herod Agrippa
  - Slew James and imprisoned Peter Acts 12
  - A grandson of Herod the Great
- Herod Agrippa II
  - Before whom Paul was tried Acts 25:13ff
  - A great-grandson of Herod the Great

A Remez?

- Why are the stories in this order?
- Chapter 12
  - Jesus is rejected by Israel.
- Chapter 13
  - Seven kingdom parables: the Church
- Chapter 14
  - A layer of insight beyond the direct narrative?

A Remez?

- Herod is a usurper, the king of this age, who is living in open adultery Jas 4:4
- He slaughters a prophet at the request of woman Rev 18:24
- John was the closing of the Old Testament.

A Remez?

- Next, people were fed in the wilderness. With 12 baskets left over, a Jewish symbol. Rev 7
- The Lord deliberately sets them up in a boat in the middle of the Sea.
  - Boats typologically after the one great boat, Noah's ark. "Kefar" in Genesis is translated "pitched;" however, everywhere else it is translated "atonement."
- The Sea is a type of Gentile nations. Dan 7

A Remez?

- The Lord is praying for them upon a mountain.
  - A mountain is a type of government Dan 2 Jesus is on the mountain, interceding for a boat in a stormy sea.
- Peter is a called out one *(ecclesia?)*
  - While the called out assembly is focused on Him they are fine, but when they take their eyes off Him they sink.

Traditions of Judaism vs. Commandments of God

Matthew 15

"Wash not their hands"

The Bible does have laws for the priests, yet here we are dealing with the everyday orthodox Jew, of which there is nothing about washing your hands in this sense in the Old Testament.

In Pharisaical Judaism, they added oral traditions which were put above the written statutes of the Torah.

Corban

- There was a tradition that goods could be set aside for either of two purposes:
  - As a dedication to the Temple, or
  - In reserve for the performance of a vow
  - Designated **korba/n** *korban,* a gift offered (or to be offered) to God; a sacred treasury, Mark 7:11
- "Corban" was excluded from any other requirements.
- They used this tradition as a ruse to evade the commandment to care for their father and their mother.

The Lengthening Tethers

• Mosaic Judaism	*Torah*
• Pharisaical Judaism	400 BC…
• Talmudic Judaism	300 – 600 AD
• Kaballah	12th Century
• Hasidic Judaism	18th Century

Feeding the Multitudes

The 5,000
Matthew. 14:15–21

- **Predominantly Jews**
- **Took place in Galilee, Bethsaida**
- **5 loaves, 2 fish**
- **12 baskets left over**
- **In the spring of the year**
- **Crowd with Him one day**

The 4,000
Matthew 15:32–39

- **Predominantly Gentiles**
- **Took place at Decapolis ***
- **7 loaves, "a few fish"**
- **7 baskets left over**
- **In the summer**
- **Crowd with Him three days**

*** Mark 8:31ff**

MATTHEW- SESSION 10: Chapters 14 & 15

1) Name the son, grandson, and great-grandson of Herod the Great, and the main Biblical events associated with each of the four.

2) Who were the two women named Salome in the New Testament?

3) What was "corban" and how was it abused?

4) Summarize five forms of Judaism and how they differ.

5) Summarize the two miraculous feedings in these chapters and how they differed.

Preparation for the Next Session:

Read Matthew 16 & 17. Review Revelation 11.

Group Discussion Questions: See the *Small Group Leaders* section of this workbook.

Session 11

The Gospel of

Matthew

Chapters 16 & 17

Matthew 16

The Pharisees also with the Sadducees came, and tempting desired him that he would shew them a sign from heaven.

He answered and said unto them, When it is evening, ye say, *It will be* fair weather: for the sky is red.

And in the morning, *It will be* foul weather to day: for the sky is red and lowring. O *ye* hypocrites, ye can discern the face of the sky; but can ye not *discern* the signs of the times?

Matthew 16:1-3

Do ye not yet understand, neither remember the five loaves of the five thousand, and how many baskets ye took up?

Neither the seven loaves of the four thousand, and how many baskets ye took up?

Matthew 16:9,10

When Jesus came into the coasts of Caesarea Philippi, he asked his disciples, saying, Whom do men say that I the Son of man am?

And they said, Some *say that thou art* John the Baptist: some, Elias; and others, Jeremias, or one of the prophets.

He saith unto them, But whom say ye that I am?

And Simon Peter answered and said, Thou art the Christ, the Son of the living God.

Matthew 16:13-16

Then said Jesus unto his disciples, If any *man* will come after me, let him deny himself, and take up his cross, and follow me.

For whosoever will save his life shall lose it: and whosoever will lose his life for my sake shall find it.

For what is a man profited, if he shall gain the whole world, and lose his own soul? or what shall a man give in exchange for his soul?

Matthew 16:24-26

For the Son of man shall come in the glory of his Father with his angels; and then he shall reward every man according to his works.
Verily I say unto you, There be some standing here, which shall not taste of death, till they see the Son of man coming in his kingdom.
Matthew 16:27,28

Matthew 17

Why Moses and Elijah?

- Two suggestions: These two men characterize two different things.
- The Law and The Prophets. The Law came by Moses, the Prophet Elijah was a uniquely empowered prophet. Other prophets were powerful in their writings but Elijah called down fire from heaven, shut the rain off for 3 ½ years! Mentioned by our Lord (Luke 4:25) and His brother James. (Jas 5:17)

Future Kingdom in View?

- All the elements of the future Kingdom are here in Matthew 17.
- We have Jesus in glory, not His humiliation.
- Moses is in glory, also radiant and shining, he represents the redeemed through death.
  Matt 13:43; Luke 9:30-34
- Elijah is there in glory, and he represents those that have entered the kingdom through the translation or rapture.
  1 Cor 15:50-51; 1 Thess 4:13-17

Identities

- 3 were expected: John 1:20,21
  - Messiah — Mal 3:1-3, 5,6
  - Elijah — Mal 4:5,6
  - Moses — Deut 18:15-19
- John the Baptist: "I am not."
  John 1:19,20; Mt 11:14; 17:10-11
  - He did not "turn the hearts of the children" as Malachi predicted, nor usher in the "great and dreadful day," etc.

Unique Powers

- Elijah
  - Fire from heaven — 1 Kgs 18:37; 2 Kgs 1:10,12; Jer 5:14
  - Shut heaven 3 1/2 years! — 1 Kgs 17:1; Luk 4:25; Jas 5:17,18
- Moses
  - Water into blood: Ex 7:19,20
  - Plagues — Ex 8 – 12

Alternatives

- Enoch?
  - "Once to die…?" Heb 9:27
    General rule; exceptions: Lazarus, Jairus' daughter, Nain's son, et al
  - The Witnesses are Jewish
    - Is Enoch a model of the Rapture?
    - Born, translated, on the Feast of Shavout?
- John, the Apostle (and writer)?
- John the Baptist?

The Two Witnesses

Revelation 11

- Temple measured 11:1,2
  - Outer Court to Gentiles: 42 months
- Two Witnesses 11:2-18
  - Empowered: 1260 days
  - Call down fire from heaven] Elijah?
  - Shut heaven, no rain]
  - Turn water into blood] Moses?
  - Smite earth with plagues]
- Beast from the Abousso kills them
  - "Earth-dwellers" celebrate
  - Resurrected after 3 ½ days

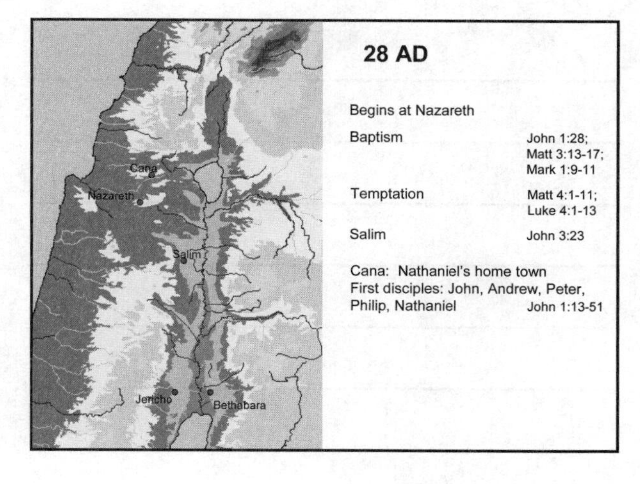

28 AD

Begins at Nazareth	
Baptism	John 1:28; Matt 3:13-17; Mark 1:9-11
Temptation	Matt 4:1-11; Luke 4:1-13
Salim	John 3:23
Cana: Nathaniel's home town First disciples: John, Andrew, Peter, Philip, Nathaniel	John 1:13-51

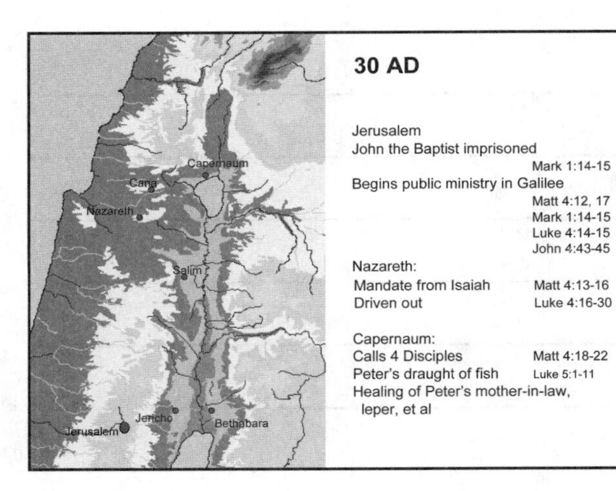

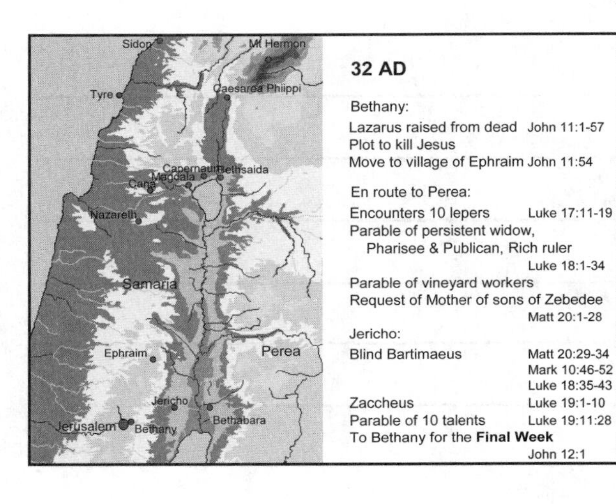

- **The lesson here is very straightforward. They could not make their witness effective here due to unbelief. Pray and fasting, self-denial.**
- **The Lord makes it clear that they should have been able to heal the child. The capacity of them to serve God was constrained by their unbelief.**
- **Your faith is not an inhibitor to the Lord causing someone to be healed. The Lord healed people who were dead (Jarius' daughter, Lazarus). It is the power of Jesus Christ that heals, not someone's faith. Don't jump to the conclusion that a Christian is ill due to their lack of faith! That would be a misapplication. Paul the apostle was not healed of his affliction although three times he prayed for healing. Was his faith lacking? The Lord may choose not to heal someone. That doesn't mean that your lack of faith might be an impediment to His healing you, but His not healing you is not a proof that you lack the faith. It is a necessary but not sufficient solution. The Lord may have some other purpose in mind.**

MATTHEW- SESSION 11: Chapters 16 & 17

1) Describe the differences between: a) Pharisees; b) Sadducees; c) Herodians

2) What was "the sign of the Prophet Jonah"? What does it tell us of the Messiah?

3) Summarize the differences between the feedings: a) Of the 4000; b) Of the 5000
What are the implications?

4) Discuss the implications of each of the words in "I will build my church."

5) Why do some believe the Transfiguration occurred at the time of Succoth?

6) What did the appearance of Moses and Elijah at the Transfiguration signify? How does this compare with the Two Witnesses in Revelation 11? List the typological significance of each of the parties present.

7) List the alternative candidates for the Two Witnesses which appear in Revelation 11 and highlight the suggestive evidences for each.

8) Were Jesus and His disciples liable for the tax mentioned in this session? Why was it paid?

Preparation for the Next Session:

Read Matthew 18.

Group Discussion Questions: See the *Small Group Leaders* section of this workbook.

Session 12

The Gospel of

Matthew

Chapter 18

Gospel of Judas?

- This text was discovered in Egypt about 1978.
- It is written in Coptic, the language of ancient Egypt, especially Christian Egypt, up to the 9th century.
- It is a codex (book with pages) rather than a scroll. The pages are badly damaged, so that there are some lacunae (blank spaces) that are difficult to fill. But it is not hard to see what it is about.

"Gnostic Gospels"

- Not "gospels" at all, but rather speculative opinions, totally devoid of any verifiable facts.
- All written under false pseudonyms in an attempt to gain legitimacy.
  - The early church rejected any documents under pseudonyms as being inconsistent with the concept of God-breathed inspiration.
- They were all written several centuries after the Gospel period - in contrast to the contemporaneous eyewitness accounts in the New Testament.

"Gnostic Gospels"

- A large number of spurious documents emerged during the centuries following the ministries of the Apostles and were universally rejected by the early church.
- Copies of a group of these were found at Nag Hammadi in Egypt in 1945, dating from the 3rd and 4th centuries.
  - These include *The Gospel of Thomas, The Gospel of Philip, The Gospel of Mary, The Gospel of Truth*, and about four dozen others.

frauds
heresey

Gnosticism – to know

- Gnosticism was a heresy that was rampant in the Roman Empire from about the 2nd century.
- Its name came from the Greek word for knowledge, *gnosis*.
- The Gnostics believed that knowledge was the way to salvation. For this reason, Gnosticism was condemned as false and heretical by several writers of the New Testament.
- The Gnostics consisted of diverse groups, from high-minded ascetics to licentious charlatans.

object was to depersonalize God

Gnosticism

- It claims that we are all divine (we have a spark of the divine in us), we are trapped in the physical world which is evil, and Jesus came to give us *knowledge* of how to escape this world and get back to the Kingdom of Light where we belong.
- In Gnosticism, salvation is by *knowledge* of mysteries, rather than by faith in the atoning work of Jesus Christ.

Gnosticism

- Gnostic literature speaks of the deities or powers of the universe, such as Yaldabaoth, Seth, Barbelo (an emanation of the Supreme Being), Sophia, and others.
- Gnostic books have complex myths of creation, involving emanations from the Supreme Being, multiple heavens with their rulers, angels, etc.
- Most of them see matter as evil, and believe that Jesus only appeared to have flesh—that His physical body was a mere phantom.
- Christ is just a *principle* in Gnosticism, rather than a *person*.

2 Tim 4
* Col. 2:8

The Nature of Angels

- Always appear in human form
  - Sodom and Gomorrah
  - Resurrection; Ascension
  - Spoke, took men by hand, ate meals
- Capable of direct physical combat
  - Passover in Egypt
  - Slaughter of 185,000 Syrians — 1 angel
- [*Demons always seek embodiment*]

always in twos

Are Children Saved?

- Are small children saved if they die before the age of accountability?
- One can build a strong Biblical case supporting this idea:

2 Sam 12:23; *
Rom 7:9

outside law I was alive
referring to childhood before
age of accountability

I shall go to him, not he to me
Job - first & last chapter
didn't dbl children - others are waiting in heaven for Job

Due Process

- Management by Hearsay (gossip)
- Guilty until proven innocent
- Confrontation of accusers

"70 Times 7"

- The Sabbath for the land was six years to cultivate, the seventh to rest. Lev 25:1-7
- For 490 years Israel failed to keep the Sabbath year of the land.
- Since they failed to keep the Sabbath of the land for 490 years, the Lord said you owe me 70 and sent them into captivity in Babylon. He forgave them for 70 X 7 times and then called what was due. 2 Chr 36:21

Forgiveness

- Forgiveness:
  - Never remembers our sin Heb 10:17
  - Restorative forgiveness 1 John 1:9
  - Discipline retained 2 Sam 13,14
  - Forgive others Col 3:13
- Degrees of Punishment:
  Luke 12:47, 48; John 13:7; Rom 2:12; 1 John 5:17

Chronology

- Tiberius appointed: 14 AD
  - Augustus died August 19, 14 AD
- (Within the) 15th year of Tiberius Luke 3:1
- Thus, ministry began in fall 28 AD
- 4th Passover: April 6, 32 AD
  Sir Robert Anderson's dating
- Other chronologies assume a Friday crucifixion

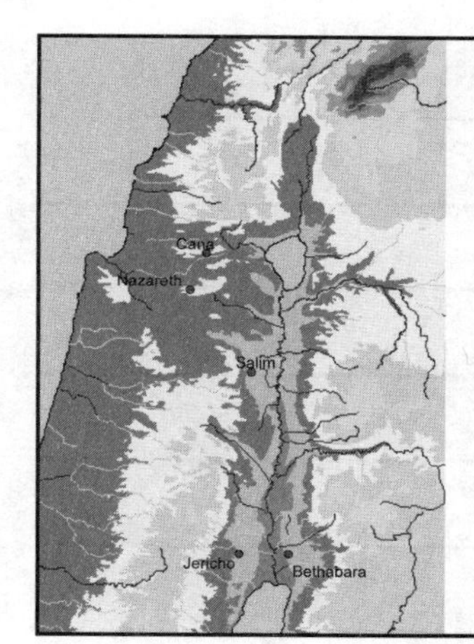

Autumn 28 AD

Begins at Nazareth

Baptism John 1:28; Matt 3:13-17; Mark 1:9-11

Temptation Matt 4:1-11; Luke 4:1-13

Salim John 3:23

Cana: Nathaniel's home town
First disciples: John, Andrew, Peter, Philip, Nathaniel John 1:13-51

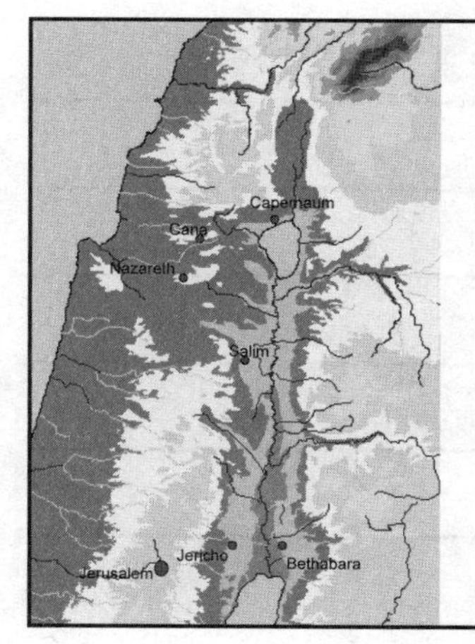

29 AD

First Miracle: the Wedding at Cana John 2:1-12

Moves to Capernaurm John 2:12

Jerusalem:
Purging of the Temple John 2:12-25
Nicodemus' visit John 3:1-21
Tarried, baptized John 3:22
John the Baptist's last testimony John 3:22-36

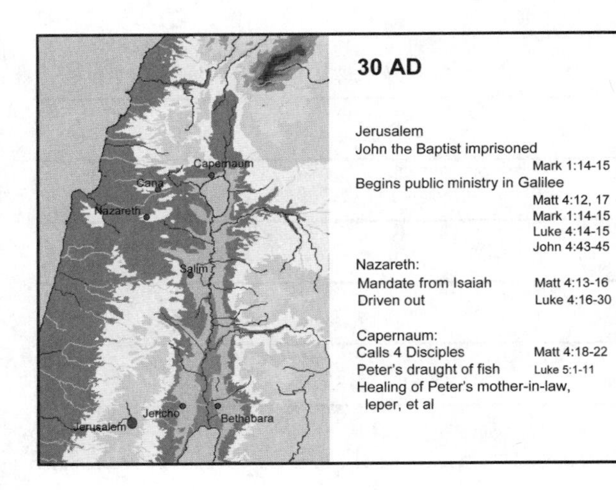
30 AD
Jerusalem
John the Baptist imprisoned
Mark 1:14-15
Begins public ministry in Galilee
Matt 4:12, 17
Mark 1:14-15
Luke 4:14-15
John 4:43-45
Nazareth:
Mandate from Isaiah Matt 4:13-16
Driven out Luke 4:16-30
Capernaum:
Calls 4 Disciples Matt 4:18-22
Peter's draught of fish Luke 5:1-11
Healing of Peter's mother-in-law, leper, et al
Capernaum
Cana
Nazareth
Salim
Jerusalem
Jericho
Bethabara

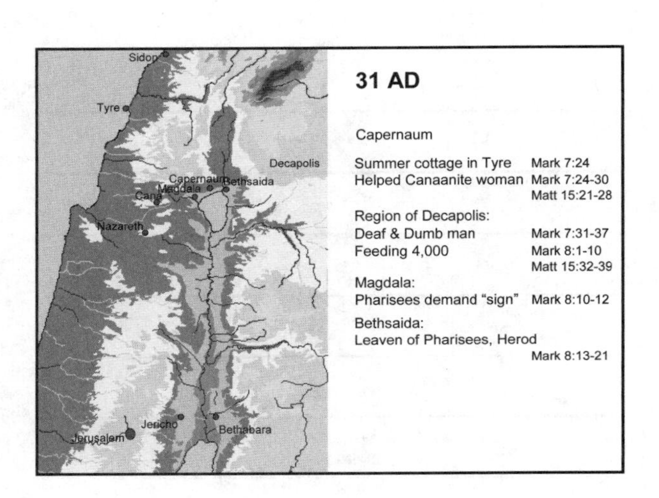
31 AD
Capernaum
Summer cottage in Tyre Mark 7:24
Helped Canaanite woman Mark 7:24-30
Matt 15:21-28
Region of Decapolis:
Deaf & Dumb man Mark 7:31-37
Feeding 4,000 Mark 8:1-10
Matt 15:32-39
Magdala:
Pharisees demand "sign" Mark 8:10-12
Bethsaida:
Leaven of Pharisees, Herod
Mark 8:13-21
Sidon
Tyre
Decapolis
Capernaum
Bethsaida
Magdala
Cana
Nazareth
Jerusalem
Jericho
Bethabara

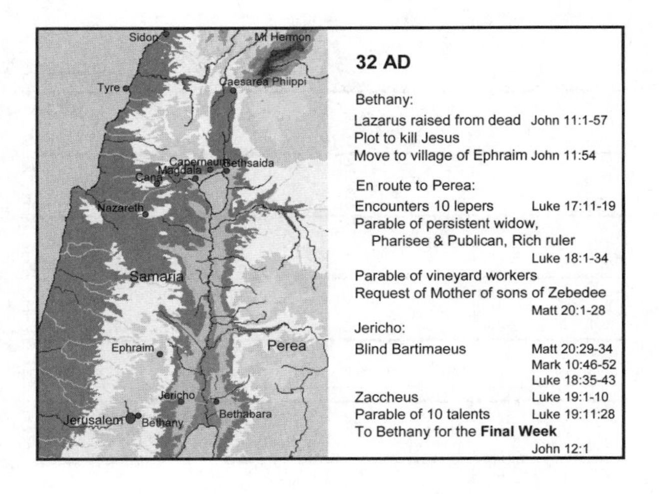
32 AD
Bethany:
Lazarus raised from dead John 11:1-57
Plot to kill Jesus
Move to village of Ephraim John 11:54
En route to Perea:
Encounters 10 lepers Luke 17:11-19
Parable of persistent widow, Pharisee & Publican, Rich ruler
Luke 18:1-34
Parable of vineyard workers
Request of Mother of sons of Zebedee
Matt 20:1-28
Jericho:
Blind Bartimaeus Matt 20:29-34
Mark 10:46-52
Luke 18:35-43
Zaccheus Luke 19:1-10
Parable of 10 talents Luke 19:11:28
To Bethany for the **Final Week**
John 12:1
Sidon
Mt Hermon
Tyre
Caesarea Philippi
Capernaum
Bethsaida
Magdala
Cana
Nazareth
Samaria
Ephraim
Perea
Jericho
Jerusalem
Bethany
Bethabara

MATTHEW- SESSION 12: Chapter 18

1) Why was the "Gospel of Judas" rejected by the early church?

2) List the defects that all the "Gnostic Gospels" have in common.

3) Are "guardian angels" a Scriptural concept? Give examples.

4) What are the distinctives between (fallen) angels and demons?

5) Are small children "saved"? Give relevant references in both Old Testament and New Testament supporting your view.

6) What are the steps to take in dealing with a "trespass" (or tort) of a brother in Christ?

7) What did Jesus mean by "seventy times seven"?

8) What was the lesson in the parable of the unforgiving steward? How do we apply this to ourselves?

Preparation for the Next Session:

Read Matthew 19 & 20.

Group Discussion Questions: See the *Small Group Leaders* section of this workbook.

Session 13

The Gospel of

Matthew

Chapters 19 & 20

Gospel of Judas

- Not a new discovery (even though it was lost for about 1,700 years).
- 180 AD: Irenaeus knew of this book and condemned it as heretical.

Matthew 19

The King's Instructions

And it came to pass, that when Jesus had finished these sayings, he departed from Galilee, and came into the coasts of Judaea beyond Jordan;

And great multitudes followed him; and he healed them there.

The Pharisees also came unto him, tempting him, and saying unto him, Is it lawful for a man to put away his wife for every cause?

Matthew 19:1-3

The Characteristics of Marriage

It is a divinely appointed union.

No court of law can change what God has established.

It is a physical union.

The man and woman become "one flesh."

It is a permanent union.

God's Law requires that the husband and wife enter into marriage without reservations. God's original Law knows nothing of "trial marriages."

It is a union between one man and one woman.

Any variations are contrary to the will of God, no matter what psychologists and jurists may say.

Marriage

- Basis for Marriage:
  1) Biological
  2) Psychological
  3) Sociological
  4) Supernatural
- God uses the marriage relationship to communicate His precious truths, namely the relationship between Christ and the Church. Eph 5:31,32
- Adam as a "type" of Christ Gen 3; 1 Tim 2:14
- Fornication before wedlock Deut 22:13,14,20,21

He saith unto him, Which? Jesus said, Thou shalt do no murder, Thou shalt not commit adultery, Thou shalt not steal, Thou shalt not bear false witness,

Honour thy father and *thy* mother: and, Thou shalt love thy neighbour as thyself.

The young man saith unto him, All these things have I kept from my youth up: what lack I yet?

Matthew 19:18-20

And every one that hath forsaken houses, or brethren, or sisters, or father, or mother, or wife, or children, or lands, for my name's sake, shall receive an hundredfold, and shall inherit everlasting life.

But many *that are* first shall be last; and the last *shall be* first.

Matthew 19:29,30

Matthew 20

For the kingdom of heaven is like unto a man that is an householder, which went out early in the morning to hire labourers into his vineyard.
And when he had agreed with the labourers for a penny a day, he sent them into his vineyard.
Matthew 20:1,2

dhna,rion *denarion*, the principal silver coin of the Roman empire.

My Wage

I bargained with life for a penny,
And life would pay no more,
However I begged at evening
When I counted my scanty store;

For life is just employer,
He gives you what you ask,
But once you have set the wages,
Why, you must bear the task.

My Wage

I worked for a menial's hire,
Only to learn, dismayed,
That any wage I had asked of life,
Life would have paid.

Jessie B. Rittenhouse

And as they departed from Jericho, a great multitude followed him.

And, behold, two blind men sitting by the way side, when they heard that Jesus passed by, cried out, saying, Have mercy on us, O Lord, *thou* Son of David.

And the multitude rebuked them, because they should hold their peace: but they cried the more, saying, Have mercy on us, O Lord, *thou* Son of David.

Matthew 20:29-31

And Jesus stood still, and called them, and said, What will ye that I shall do unto you?

They say unto him, Lord, that our eyes may be opened.

So Jesus had compassion *on them*, and touched their eyes: and immediately their eyes received sight, and they followed him.

Matthew 20:32-34

Similar Accounts

Cf. Matthew 20:29-34; Luke18:35-43; Mark10:46-52

- Luke: as they came to Jericho, they met the one beggar as they entered the city.
  - Both Matthew and Mark indicate that the healing took place as they were leaving.
- Mark and Luke describe one blind man; Matthew describes two. How many were there? Two.
  - Mark and Luke focus on the one who had a better witness
- Two blind men healed just before the twelve were sent out to the Kingdom of Israel. Matthew 9
- Two blind men healed at the close of the Galilean ministry and just before the Triumphal entry. Matthew 20

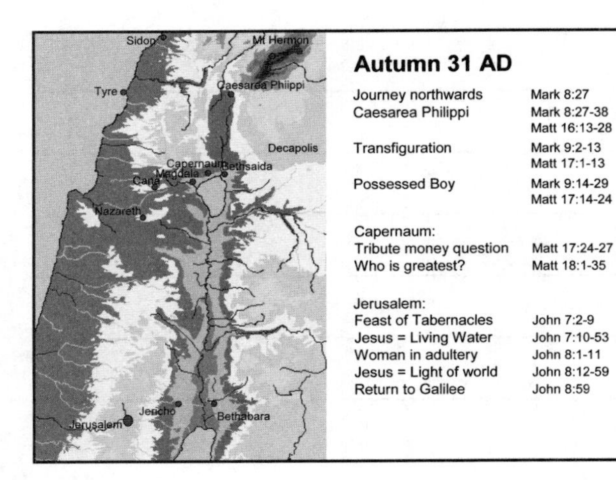
Sidon
Mt Hermon
Tyre
Caesarea Philippi
Decapolis
Capernaum
Bethsaida
Magdala
Cana
Nazareth
Jericho
Jerusalem
Bethabara
Autumn 31 AD
Journey northwards Mark 8:27
Caesarea Philippi Mark 8:27-38 Matt 16:13-28
Transfiguration Mark 9:2-13 Matt 17:1-13
Possessed Boy Mark 9:14-29 Matt 17:14-24
Capernaum:
Tribute money question Matt 17:24-27
Who is greatest? Matt 18:1-35
Jerusalem:
Feast of Tabernacles John 7:2-9
Jesus = Living Water John 7:10-53
Woman in adultery John 8:1-11
Jesus = Light of world John 8:12-59
Return to Galilee John 8:59

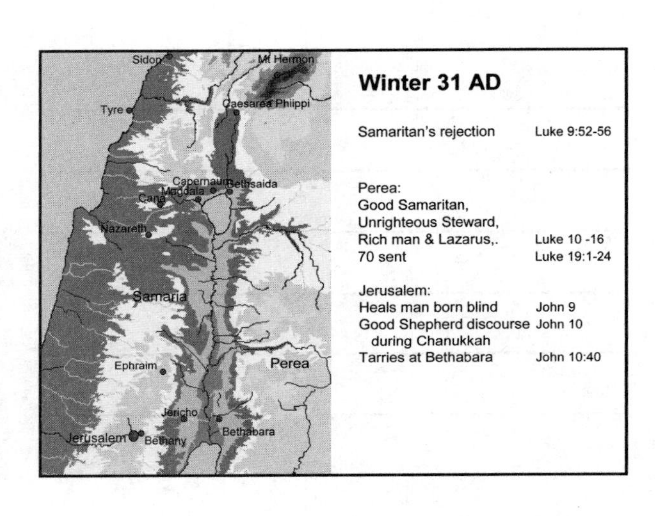
Sidon
Mt Hermon
Tyre
Caesarea Philippi
Capernaum
Bethsaida
Magdala
Cana
Nazareth
Samaria
Ephraim
Perea
Jericho
Jerusalem
Bethany
Bethabara
Winter 31 AD
Samaritan's rejection Luke 9:52-56
Perea:
Good Samaritan,
Unrighteous Steward,
Rich man & Lazarus,. Luke 10 -16
70 sent Luke 19:1-24
Jerusalem:
Heals man born blind John 9
Good Shepherd discourse John 10
during Chanukkah
Tarries at Bethabara John 10:40

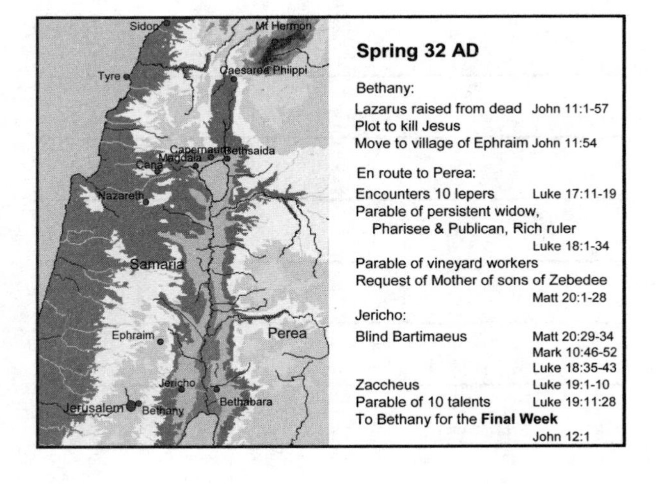
Sidon
Mt Hermon
Tyre
Caesarea Philippi
Capernaum
Bethsaida
Magdala
Cana
Nazareth
Samaria
Ephraim
Perea
Jericho
Jerusalem
Bethany
Bethabara
Spring 32 AD
Bethany:
Lazarus raised from dead John 11:1-57
Plot to kill Jesus
Move to village of Ephraim John 11:54
En route to Perea:
Encounters 10 lepers Luke 17:11-19
Parable of persistent widow,
Pharisee & Publican, Rich ruler
Luke 18:1-34
Parable of vineyard workers
Request of Mother of sons of Zebedee
Matt 20:1-28
Jericho:
Blind Bartimaeus Matt 20:29-34 Mark 10:46-52 Luke 18:35-43
Zaccheus Luke 19:1-10
Parable of 10 talents Luke 19:11:28
To Bethany for the Final Week
John 12:1

MATTHEW- SESSION 13: Chapters 19 & 20

1) Why did Moses provide for a "writing of divorcement"? What was its purpose?

2) Explain the supernatural basis of marriage. Give Biblical examples in which God uses it to communicate.

3) What was the principal lesson of the householder's wage policies?

4) What were the lessons Jesus gave concerning organizational hierarchy in the church?

5) Contrast the healing of the blind men in Matthew 20:29-34, Luke18:35-43, and Mark 10:46-52. Are they conflicting accounts? Reconcile the differences.

Preparation for the Next Session:

The Triumphal Entry: Beginning of the Final Week…

Read: Matthew 21:1-11; Mark 11:1-10; Luke 19:29-44; and John 12:12-19.
(Why is this *not* "Palm Sunday"?)

Group Discussion Questions: See the *Small Group Leaders* section of this workbook.

Session 14

The Gospel of

Matthew

Chapter 21
Triumphal Entry

The Triumphal Entry

Rejoice greatly, O daughter of Zion; shout, O daughter of Jerusalem: behold, thy King cometh unto thee: He is just, and having salvation; lowly, and riding upon an ass, and upon a colt the foal of an ass.

Zechariah 9:9

Hosanna

- This Greek transliteration of a Hebrew word "Save we pray," occurs 6 times in the Gospels as the cry of the people when our Lord entered Jerusalem as the Messiah.
  Mt 21:9,15; Mk 11:9; Jn 12:13
- Taken from Ps. 118, recited at the Feast of Tabernacles in "the great Hallel," Ps. 113-118 they waved willow and palm branches with rejoicings.
- The 7th or last day of the feast was called "the Great Hosanna," especially associated with consummated salvation.

Final Week

Matthew 21	Luke 19	Triumphal Entry
Matthew 22	Luke 20	
Matthew 23		
Matthew 24	Luke 21	Olivet Discourse
Matthew 25		
Matthew 26	Luke 22	Last Seder
Matthew 27	Luke 23	Crucifixion
Matthew 28	Luke 24	Resurrection

Luke 19

Daniel 9

The 70 Weeks

Old Testament (*Tenach*) Texts

- Original Hebrew ("*Vorlage*")
  - In the days of Ezra and Nehemiah
- Septuagint Translation (LXX)
  - 285-270 BC, Ptolemy Philadelphus II commissioned 70 top scholars at Alexandria to translate the Hebrew *Tenach* (Old Testament) into the common Greek of that day
  - *Primary text quoted in the New Testament*
- Masoretic Text (MT)
  - Derived from the Council of Jamnia, 90 AD

The "70 Weeks" of Daniel

The Scope	9:24
The 69 Weeks	9:25
(The Interval)	9:26
The 70th Week	9:27

"Weeks" = ?

Days:	Sabbath on the 7th Day	Gen 2:2; Ex 20:11
Weeks:	Feast of Weeks	Lev 23:15,16
Months:	Nisan to Tishri	Ex 12:2; Lev 23:24
Years:	Sabbatical Years for the Land	Lev 25:1-22; 26:33-35 Deut 15; Ex 23:10,11; 2 Chr 36:19-21

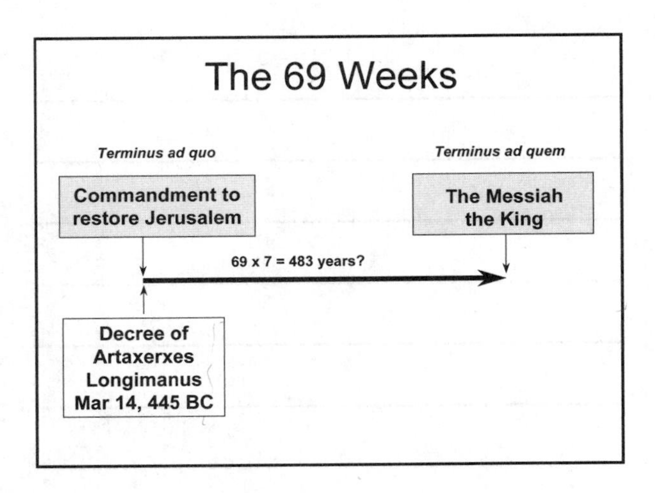
The 69 Weeks
Terminus ad quo
Terminus ad quem
Commandment to restore Jerusalem
The Messiah the King
69 x 7 = 483 years?
Decree of Artaxerxes Longimanus Mar 14, 445 BC

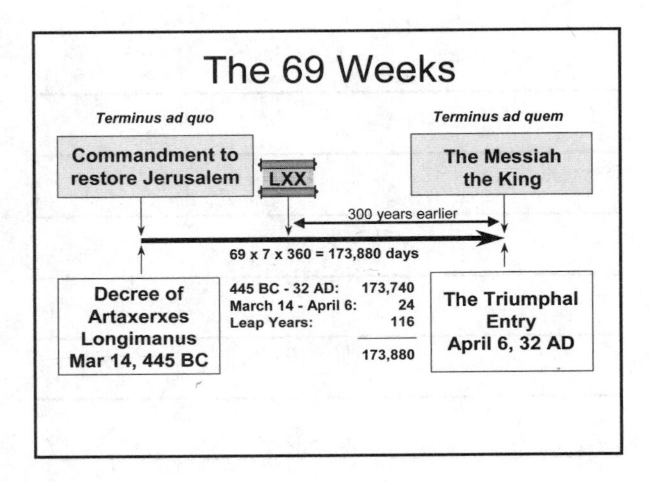
The 69 Weeks
Terminus ad quo
Terminus ad quem
Commandment to restore Jerusalem
LXX
The Messiah the King
300 years earlier
69 x 7 x 360 = 173,880 days
Decree of Artaxerxes Longimanus Mar 14, 445 BC
445 BC - 32 AD: 173,740
March 14 - April 6: 24
Leap Years: 116
173,880
The Triumphal Entry April 6, 32 AD

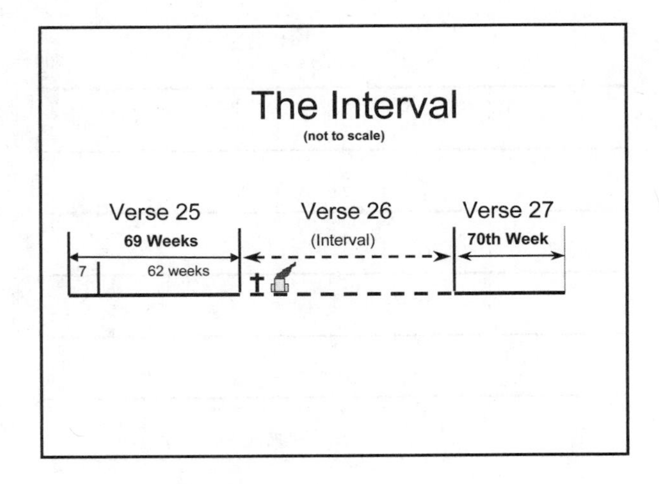
The Interval
(not to scale)
Verse 25
69 Weeks
7
62 weeks
Verse 26
(Interval)
Verse 27
70th Week

Divisions of Theology

• Bibliology	The Bible
• Theology Proper	Attributes of God
• Christology	Lord Jesus Christ
• Pneumatology	Holy Spirit
• Angelology	Angels, fallen and unfallen
• Anthropology	Man
• Soteriology	Salvation
• Ecclesiology	The Church
• Eschatology	End-Times; Last Things
• Israelology	Israel as God's instrument

Israel and the Church

- Distinctions
  - Different Origins, Missions, Destinies
- "Replacement" views deny Israel its place in God's program Romans 9, 10, 11
  - Would seem to make God a Liar
  - Laid the basis for Christian Anti-Semitism
- The "70 Weeks" deal specifically with *Israel*
- Paul's trichotomy: Jews, Gentiles, Church 1 Cor 10:32
- Distinctives reappear after Revelation 4

The Church Interval

- **Interval also implied:** Isa 61:1,2 (re: Lk 4:18-20); Rev 12:5,6. Also: Isa 54:7; Hos 3:4,5; Amos 9:10,11; (Acts 15:13-18); Micah 5:2,3; Zech 9:9,10; Luke 1:31,32; 21:24
- **Interval defined:** Luke 19:42 *until* Rom 11:25
- **This interval is the period of the Church, an era kept secret in OT:** Mt 13:34,35; Eph 3:5,9

The Church

- Prerequisites:
  - Atonement: Mt 16:18, 21
  - Resurrection: Eph 1:20-23
  - Ascension: Eph 4:7-11
    (Spiritual gifts only after ascension)
- Born at Pentecost: Col 1:18
  1 Cor 12:13
  Acts 1:5, 11:15-16

Mystery Character

- Body Concept Eph 3:3-5,9
- Indwelling every believer Col 1:26-27
- Bride of Christ Eph 5:22-32
- *Harpazo,* ("Rapture") 1 Cor 15:50-58
- One "New Man" Eph 2:15
  Cf. Rev 12:5
- Distinguished from Jews & Gentiles
  1 Cor 10:32

The 70th Week

And he ("the prince that shall come") shall enforce the covenant with [the] many for one week: and in the midst of the week he shall cause the sacrifice and the oblation to cease, and for the overspreading of abominations he shall make it desolate, even until the consummation, and that determined shall be poured upon the desolate.

Daniel 9:27

MATTHEW- SESSION 14: Chapter 21: 1-11

The Triumphal Entry

1) Which of the seven feasts of Moses were obligatory to be observed in Jerusalem?

2) How do we know for certain that the prophecies of the Old Testament were documented several centuries *before* the New Testament period?

3) Outline the last four verses of Daniel 9, and highlight the primary significances of each.

4) Which Sabbath failure caused the specific seventy years of captivity in Babylon? Give references.

5) How do we know that the presentation of Jesus Christ as the *Meshiach Nagid* did <u>not</u> occur on a Sunday? Why do people refer to it as "Palm Sunday"? Why did Jesus enter riding a donkey?

6) Why did the Pharisees object to the singing of Psalm 118?

7) Summarize Daniel 9:24-27. What was the context? Why was Israel in captivity for precisely 70 years? How did Daniel know that the captivity was almost over? How is this passage relevant to today?

8) Diagram the timeline of Daniel 9:25, and detail the calculations of Gabriel's prophecy to Daniel. How is this useful as a testimony of identity?

9) How do we know that the "70 weeks" were not contiguous? What events take place between the 69th and 70th "week"?

10) Explain the precision of Gabriel's announcement to Daniel. Did Jesus hold the Jewish leadership accountable? Explain.

Preparation for the Next Session:

Read the remainder of Matthew 21 and Matthew 22. In anticipation of the forthcoming sessions, begin to read carefully the passages of the Final Week in each of the four Gospels: Matthew 21-28; Mark 11-16; Luke 19-24; John 12-21 (over half of his Gospel!).

Group Discussion Questions: See the *Small Group Leaders* section of this workbook.

Session 15

The Gospel of

Matthew

Chapters 21 & 22

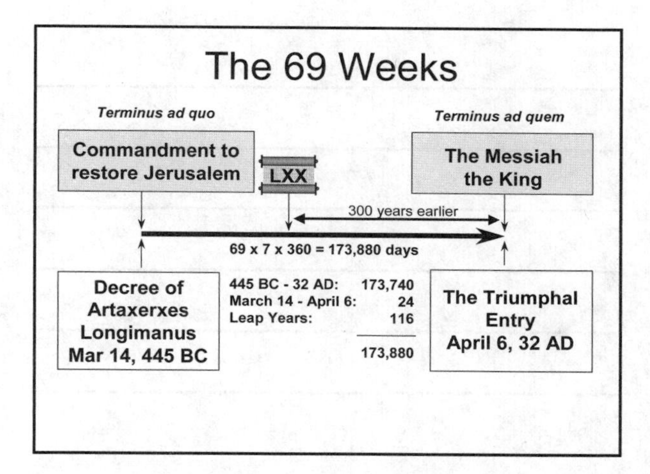

Matthew 21

Part 2

And Jesus went into the temple of God, and cast out all them that sold and bought in the temple, and overthrew the tables of the moneychangers, and the seats of them that sold doves,

And said unto them, It is written, My house shall be called the house of prayer; but ye have made it a den of thieves.

And the blind and the lame came to him in the temple; and he healed them.

Matthew 21:12-14

The Fig Tree

- Bethphage": House of unripe figs
  Luke 13:6-9; Mt 21:17-20; 24:32,33
- The fig tree symbolized the nation of Israel
  Jer. 8:13; Hosea 9:10, 16; Luke 13:6–9
- Or, specifically, Judah: Isa 24, Hos 9, Joel 1
  - Just as this tree had leaves but no fruit, so Israel had a show of religion but no practical experience of faith resulting in godly living
- *God wants to produce fruit in the lives of His people*

Now will I sing to my wellbeloved a song of my beloved touching his vineyard. My wellbeloved hath a vineyard in a very fruitful hill:

And he fenced it, and gathered out the stones thereof, and planted it with the choicest vine, and built a tower in the midst of it, and also made a winepress therein: and he looked that it should bring forth grapes, and it brought forth wild grapes.

Isaiah 5:1,2

Woe unto them that call evil good, and good evil; that put darkness for light, and light for darkness; that put bitter for sweet, and sweet for bitter!

Woe unto *them that are* wise in their own eyes, and prudent in their own sight!

Woe unto *them that are* mighty to drink wine, and men of strength to mingle strong drink:

Isaiah 5:20-22

Hear another parable: There was a certain householder, which planted a vineyard, and hedged it round about, and digged a winepress in it, and built a tower, and let it out to husbandmen, and went into a far country:

And when the time of the fruit drew near, he sent his servants to the husbandmen, that they might receive the fruits of it.

And the husbandmen took his servants, and beat one, and killed another, and stoned another.

Matthew 21:33-35

Stones & Mountains

- God is referred to as a rock or a stone. Deut. 32:4, 18, 30–31; Ps. 18:2, 31, 46
- The stone is also a messianic title.
- To Israel, Jesus was a stumbling stone. Isa. 8:14–15; Rom. 9:32–33; 1 Cor. 1:23
- Israel rejected the Messiah, but in His death and resurrection He created the church.

Stones & Mountains

- To the church, Jesus is the foundation stone, the head of the corner.
  Eph. 2:20–22; 1 Peter 2:4–5
- At the end of the age, Jesus will come as the smiting stone, destroy Gentile kingdoms, and establish His own glorious kingdom. Dan. 2:34

Matthew 22

And Jesus answered and spake unto them again by parables, and said,
The kingdom of heaven is like unto a certain king, which made a marriage for his son,
And sent forth his servants to call them that were bidden to the wedding: and they would not come.

Matthew 22:1-3

The Enemies

- The Pharisees opposed the Roman poll tax for several reasons:
  1. They did not want to submit to a Gentile power.
  2. Caesar was revered as a god .
  3. They had better uses for the money than to give it to Rome.
- Since the Herodians were the party supporting Herod, they were in favor of the tax.
  – Herod's authority was given to him by Caesar; and Herod would have had a difficult time staying in power without Rome's support.

The Enemies

- Every tax the poor people had to pay was another reminder that they were not free.
- The Zealots, an "underground" organization of fanatical Jews, often staged protests against Rome. They would oppose any Roman tax.

The Enemies

- It is easy to see why the Pharisees and Herodians chose the poll tax as the bait for their trap:
  – If he opposed the tax, he would be in trouble with Rome.
  – If he approved the tax, he would be in trouble with the Jews.

Our Dual Citizenship

- Christians must honor and obey rulers.
  Rom. 13; 1 Peter 2:13–17; 1 Tim. 2:1ff
  - Christians have a dual citizenship, in heaven and on earth. Phil. 3:20

Our Dual Citizenship

- Christians must honor and obey rulers.
- Christians must honor and obey God.
  - Caesar was not God.

Our Dual Citizenship

- Christians must honor and obey rulers.
- Christians must honor and obey God.
- Man bears God's image and owes God his all.
  - Caesar's image was on the coin; God's image is on man. Gen. 1:26–27
  - Sin has marred that image, but through Jesus Christ, it can be restored. Eph. 4:24; Col. 3:10

MATTHEW- SESSION 15: Chapters 21 (part 2) & 22

1) How are the two incidents of the cleansing of the Temple and the cursing of the fig tree related?

2) Summarize each of the parables, with their personal applications, in this session.

3) How does the vineyard and the cursed fig tree relate to us today?

4) Explain the role of the attire of the wedding guest? What was wrong here? What are the implications for us?

Preparation for the Next Session:

Read Matthew 23 and review Matthew 5.

Group Discussion Questions: See the *Small Group Leaders* section of this workbook.

Session 16

The Gospel of

Matthew

Chapter 23

Matthew 23

Our Lord's Last Public Message

False Righteousness

1. Entering the kingdom — 5:3
   - Shutting up the kingdom — 23:13
2. Mourners comforted — 5:4
   - Destroyers condemned — 23:14
3. Meek inherit the earth — 5:5
   - Proud send souls to hell — 23:15
4. Hungering for holiness — 5:6
   - Greedy for gain — 23:16–22

False Righteousness

5. Obtaining mercy 5:7
   – Rejecting mercy 23:23–24
6. Pure in heart 5:8
   – Defiled in heart 23:25–28
7. Peacemakers = God's children 5:9
   – Persecutors are the devil's children 23:29f
8. Persecuted are God's children 5:10
   – Persecutors are the devil's children 23:29f

Eight Woes

Matthew 23:13-34

Tithing

- The Old Testament Law required tithing. Lev 27:30; Deut. 14:22ff
- Abraham had practiced tithing long before the Law was given. Gen 14:20
- Jacob followed his grandfather's example. Gen 28:20–22
- The principles of Christian giving under grace. 2 Cor 8–9
- We are not content simply to give a tithe (10%), but we also want to bring offerings to the Lord out of hearts filled with love.

Matthew's Primary Theme
23:37-39

1) The Purpose of all history
2) The Tragedy of all history
3) The Triumph of all history

The Interval

And after threescore and two weeks shall Messiah be cut off, but not for himself: and the people of the prince that shall come shall destroy the city and the sanctuary; and the end thereof shall be with a flood, and unto the end of the war desolations are determined.

Daniel 9:26

כָּרַת *karat,* to cut off, eliminate, kill, execute
Daniel 9:26

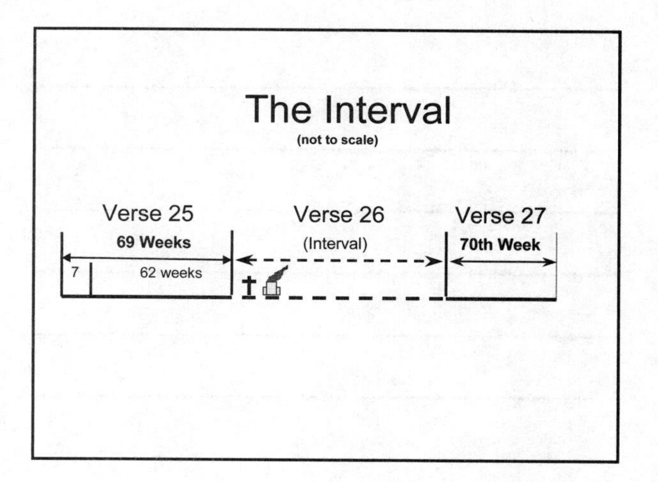

Rabbinical Confirmations

Daniel 9:26

- Messianic; prior to the Temple destroyed
  - *Yalkut,* Vol II, 32b, p.79 Nazir edition
- Messiah to exit prior to 33 AD
  - *Midrash Berishit*, p.243 Warsaw edition

re: Yakov Prasch

The Destiny of Israel

The Missing Key of "Systematic" Theology

Divisions of Theology

• Bibliology	The Bible
• Theology Proper	Attributes of God
• Christology	Lord Jesus Christ
• Pneumatology	Holy Spirit
• Angelology	Angels, fallen and unfallen
• Anthropology	Man
• Soteriology	Salvation
• Ecclesiology	The Church
• Eschatology	End-Times; Last Things
• Israelology	Israel as God's instrument

Israel and the Church

- Distinctions
  - Different Origins, Missions, Destinies
- "Replacement" views deny Israel its place in God's program Romans 9, 10, 11
  - Would seem to make God a Liar
  - Laid the basis for Christian Anti-Semitism
- The "70 Weeks" deal specifically with *Israel*
- Paul's trichotomy: Jews, Gentiles, Church 1 Cor 10:32
- Distinctives reappear after Revelation 4

The Church Interval

- **Interval also implied:** Isa 61:1,2 (re: Lk 4:18-20); Rev 12:5,6. Also: Isa 54:7; Hos 3:4,5; Amos 9:10,11; (Acts 15:13-18); Micah 5:2,3; Zech 9:9,10; Luke 1:31,32; 21:24
- **Interval defined:** Luke 19:42 *until* Rom 11:25
- **This interval is the period of the Church, an era kept secret in OT:** Mt 13:34,35; Eph 3:5,9

The Church

- Prerequisites:
  - Atonement: Mt 16:18, 21
  - Resurrection: Eph 1:20-23
  - Ascension: Eph 4:7-11
    (Spiritual gifts only after ascension)
- Born at Pentecost: Col 1:18
  1 Cor 12:13
  Acts 1:5, 11:15-16

Mystery Character

- Body Concept Eph 3:3-5,9
- Indwelling every believer Col 1:26-27
- Bride of Christ Eph 5:22-32
- *Harpazo,* ("Rapture") 1 Cor 15:50-58
- One "New Man" Eph 2:15 Cf. Rev 12:5
- Distinguished from Jews & Gentiles 1 Cor 10:32

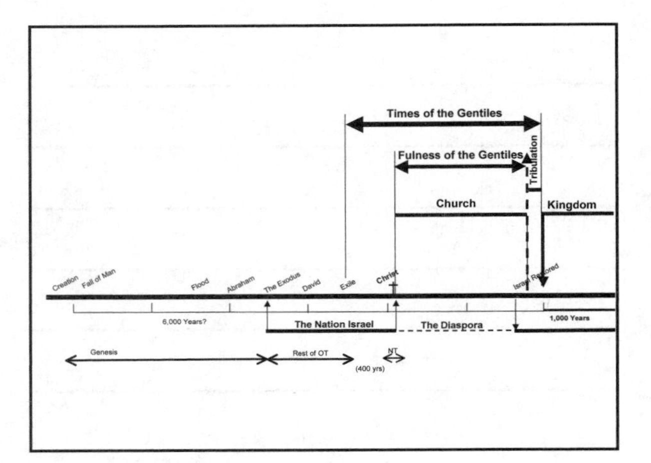

The 70th Week

And he ("the prince that shall come") shall enforce the covenant with [the] many for one week: and in the midst of the week he shall cause the sacrifice and the oblation to cease, and for the overspreading of abominations he shall make it desolate, even until the consummation, and that determined shall be poured upon the desolate.

Daniel 9:27

MATTHEW- SESSION 16: Chapter 23

1) Contrast each of the 8 woes on the Pharisees with the 8 beatitudes in Matthew 5.

2) What is: a) the Purpose of all history? b) the Tragedy of all history? c) the Triumph of all history? Explain each.

3) List the distinctives between the nation of Israel, and the Church. When will the "blindness" of Israel be lifted?

4) What defines the end of Daniel 9:26 and the beginning (and end) of Daniel 9:27?

5) Who is the "he" of Daniel 9:27? How do we know?

Preparation for the Next Session:

The famed "Olivet Discourse," one of the most important prophetic passages in the New Testament. Read Matthew 24, Mark 13 and Luke 21. Compare and note any differences.

Group Discussion Questions: See the *Small Group Leaders* section of this workbook.

Session 17

The Gospel of

Matthew

Chapter 24
Olivet Discourse

The Olivet Discourse

Matthew 24 ~
Mark 13 ~
Luke 21?

Issues

- The Destruction of Jerusalem
  - in 70 AD? Or is it yet future?
- The "Abomination of Desolation"?
  - What is it?
  - When did it happen? Or has it yet?
- The Great Tribulation
- The Parable of the Fig Tree
- (Which) "Generation shall not pass away"?
- The Doctrine of Imminence
  - For each of us individually…

Prologue

- Epistemology
  - The Study of Knowledge: Its scope & limits
- "Be Not Deceived" (How?)
  1. Establish the integrity of the Word of God & its extraterrestrial origin
  2. Establish the identity of Jesus Christ
  3. Carefully understand precisely what He said

Eschatology

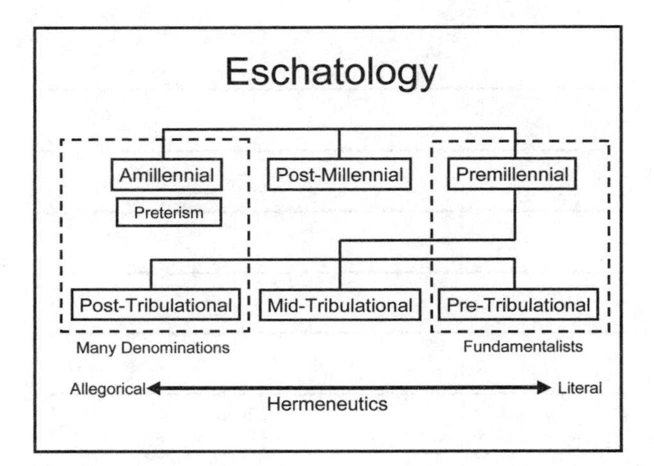

The Hazard of Presuppostions

1. Traditions & "Tangled Tethers"
   - Mosaic Judaism
   - Pharisaical Judaism
   - Talmudic Judaism
   - Kabbalistic Judaism
   - Hasidic Judaism

   Drift away from original texts
2. "Harmonization" vs Loss of Resolution
   - The Olivet Discourse: Past or Future?
   - Are they one briefing or several?

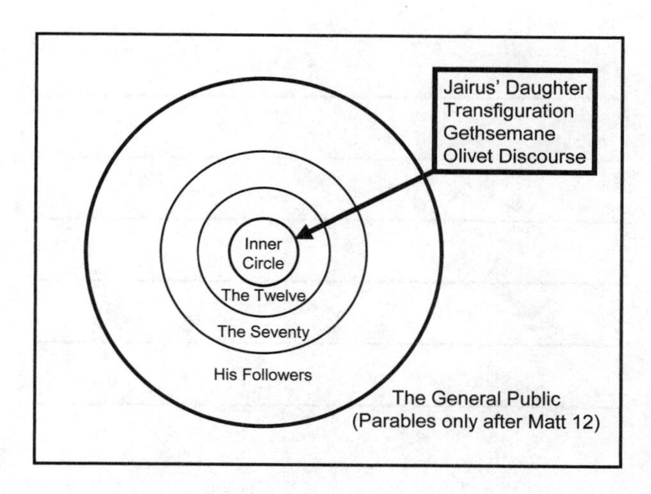

The Beginning of Sorrows

	Matthew	Luke	Revelation
• False Christs	24:4-5	21:4	6:1-2
• Wars	24:6	21:9,10	6:3-4
• Famines	24:7a	21:11	6:5-6
• Pestilences	24:7b-8	21:12	6:7-8
• Earthquakes	24:9	21:24	6:12

Historical Background

- Antiochus IV, son of Antiochus the Great, became the successor of his brother, Seleucus IV, who had been murdered by his minister, Heliodorus, as king of Syria. (175-164 BC)
- A despot; eccentric and unreliable; cruel and tyrannical.
- "Epiphanes" is an abbreviation of Greek: *theos epiphanes*, a designation he gave himself: "the god who appears or reveals himself".

Historical Background

- Antiochus undertook the total eradication of the Jewish religion and the establishment of Greek polytheism in its stead.
- The observance of all Jewish laws, especially those relating to the Sabbath and to circumcision, were forbidden under pain of death.

Antiochus IV ("Epiphanes")

- In Jerusalem on the 15th of Chislev in December 168 BC:
  - "Broke the league that he had made"
  - a pagan altar was built on the Great Altar of Burnt Sacrifices
- Stripped the Temple of its treasures

Josephus, *Antiquities*, XII v 4

Antiochus IV ("Epiphanes")

- Pillaged the city of Jerusalem
  - 10,000 captives
- Compelled them to forsake worship
- Forbid circumcision; crucified violators
- Torah forbidden & destroyed

Josephus, *Antiquities*, XII v 4

Antiochus IV ("Epiphanes")

- On the 25th of Chislev, (His birthday) sacrifice was brought on this altar for the first time

  1 Maccabees 1:54,59
- Offered a swine in every village

  Josephus, *Antiquities*, XII v 4
- Erected an idol to Zeus in the Holy of Holies
  - "a desolating sacrilege" 1 Maccabees 1:54
  - "Temple of Jupiter Olympius"

    2 Maccabees 6:1-7

Maccabean Revolt

- A spontaneous revolt was to turn into a full-scale war:
  - The arrival of officers to carry out Antiochus' decrees at the village of Modein, where an aged priest named Mattathias lived with his five sons
- When Mattathias killed both
  1. The first Jew who approached the pagan altar to offer sacrifice and
  2. The royal official who presided,

  he and his sons were fled to the hills...

Maccabean Revolt

- Mattathias and his 5 sons became the nucleus of a growing band of rebels against Antiochus:
  - John 'Gaddi,'
  - Simon 'Thassi,'
  - Judas 'Maccabeus,' ("Hammer")
  - Eleazar 'Avaran,'
  - Jonathan 'Apphus'

Maccabean Revolt

- Judas' most notable achievements:
  - the recapture of Jerusalem
    (except for the Akra fortress, where the Syrian garrison continued to hold out)
  - the rededication of the Temple, after the defiled altar had been demolished and rebuilt.
  - The rededication, on 25 Kislev of 164 BC, still celebrated as Hanukkah John 10:22
  - Antiochus' death also took place in 164

Chronology

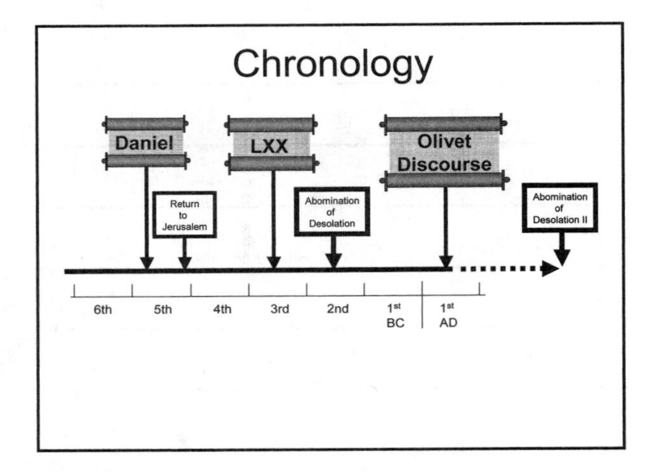

Daniel's 70th Week

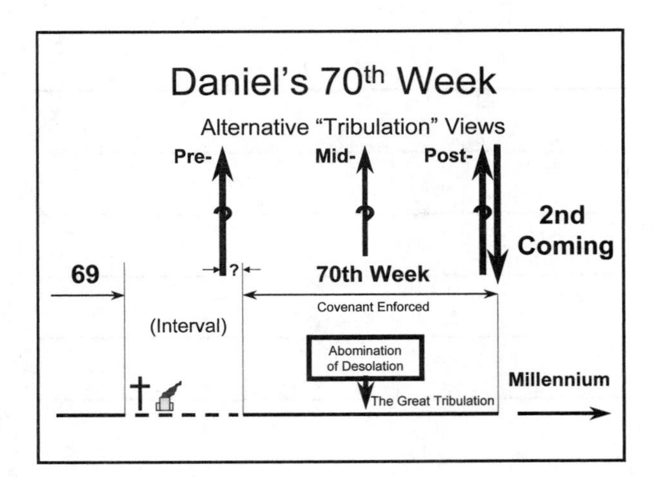

MATTHEW- SESSION 17: Chapter 24 -- Part 1

1) Where are the "Beginning of Sorrows" listed (four places)?

2) What is the "Abomination of Desolation"? How do we know? What is its location?

3) List the major hazards to sound hermeneutics.

4) Diagram the various views on eschatology and annotate their hermeneutical assumptions.

5) Diagram the epistemological approach used in this session.

6) List five "brands" of Judaism and their hermeneutical bases.

7) List the attendees to the "Olivet Discourse."

8) Explain the difference between: a) "The times of the Gentiles" b) "The fullness of the Gentiles"

9) Draw a timeline which includes the following events: a) Gabriel's prophecy given to Daniel; b) The Septuagint Translation; c) The Olivet Discourse; d) The return from the Babylonian Captivity; e) The Abomination of Desolation (2?)

10) Who is the "Goodman of the house," *oikodespotes,* in the parable of Matthew 24? Explain.

Preparation for the Next Session:

Read Luke 21 and list the differences.

Group Discussion Questions: See the *Small Group Leaders* section of this workbook.

Session 18

The Gospel of

Matthew

Chapter 24 vs. Luke 21?

The Hazard of Presuppositions

1. Traditions & "Tangled Tethers"
   - Mosaic Judaism
   - Pharisaical Judaism
   - Talmudic Judaism
   - Kabbalistic Judaism
   - Hasidic Judaism

   Drift away from original texts

2. "Harmonization" vs Loss of Resolution
   - The Olivet Discourse: Past or Future?
   - Are they one briefing or several?

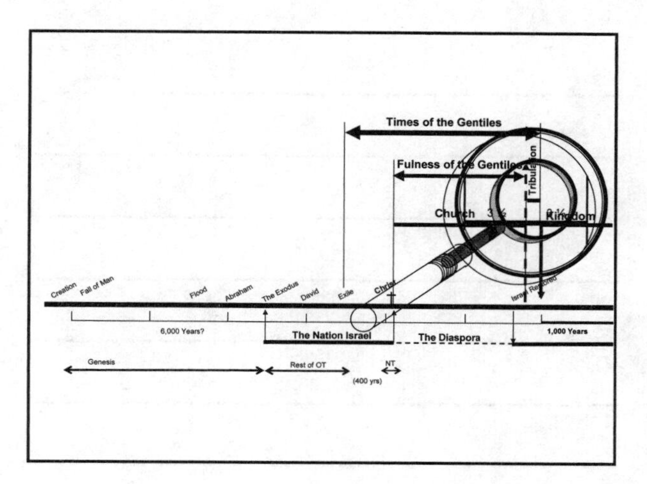

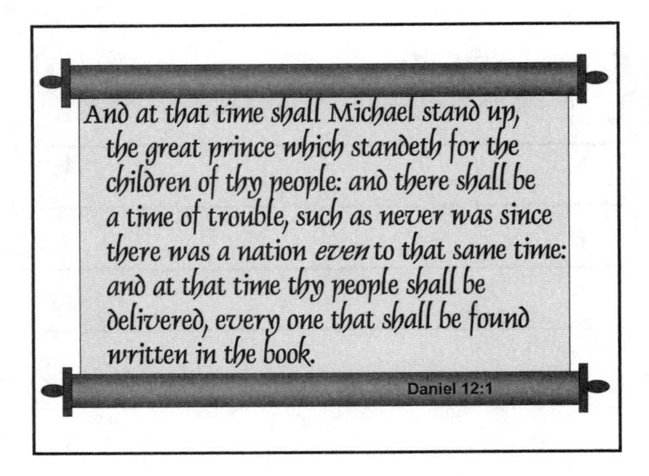
And at that time shall Michael stand up, the great prince which standeth for the children of thy people: and there shall be a time of trouble, such as never was since there was a nation *even* to that same time: and at that time thy people shall be delivered, every one that shall be found written in the book.
Daniel 12:1

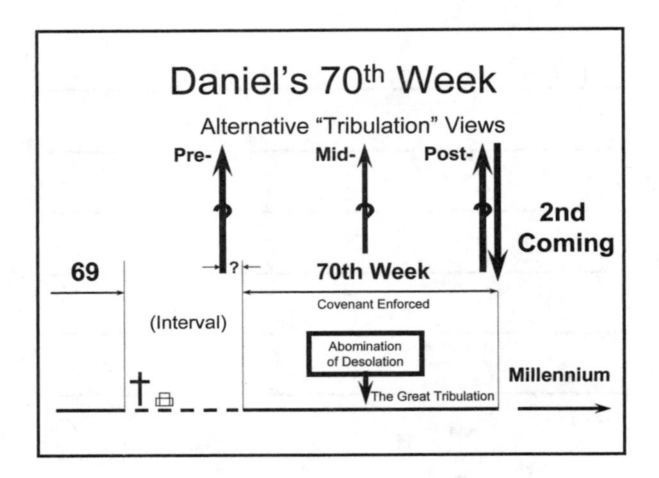
Daniel's 70th Week
Alternative "Tribulation" Views
Pre-
Mid-
Post-
2nd Coming
69
?
70th Week
Covenant Enforced
(Interval)
Abomination of Desolation
The Great Tribulation
Millennium

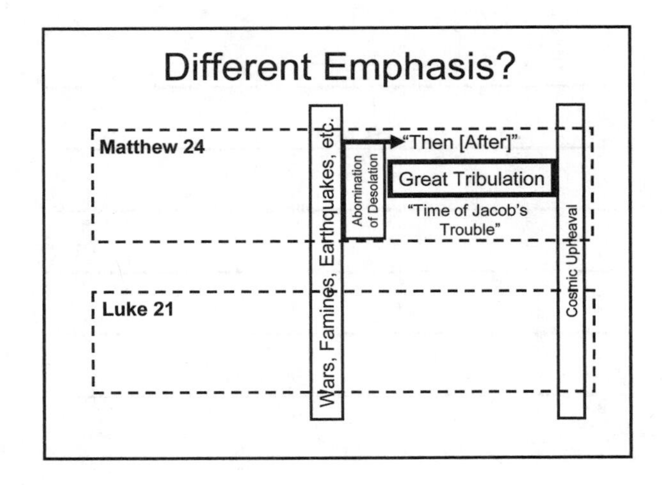
Different Emphasis?
Matthew 24
Wars, Famines, Earthquakes, etc.
Abomination of Desolation
"Then [After]"
Great Tribulation
"Time of Jacob's Trouble"
Cosmic Upheaval
Luke 21

The Beginning of Sorrows

	Matthew	Luke	Revelation
• False Christs	24:4-5	21:4	6:1-2
• Wars	24:6	21:9,10	6:3-4
• Famines	24:7a	21:11	6:5-6
• Pestilences	24:7b-8	21:12	6:7-8
• Earthquakes	24:9	21:24	6:12

The Siege of Jerusalem

- Vespasian commanded by Nero to attack Jerusalem
  - Vespasian, and his son, Titus, attack cities in the Galilee, et al
- Nero died June 68 AD;
  - Anarchy, civil war in Rome ensued
    - Galba murdered, Jan 15, 69 AD
    - Otho defeated; suicide, Apr 16, 69 AD
    - Vitelius murdered by his own troops, Dec 20
  - Vespasian succeeds as Emperor

The Siege of Jerusalem

- Titus left to complete the siege
  Josephus: *Wars* VI, vi, 1
- Christians escaped to the mountains in Pella in Perea
  Eusebius, Book III, 5.1

18 month time laspe
No Christians died in siege because they left like Luke told them to leave

And when these things begin to come to pass, then look up, and lift up your heads; for your redemption draweth nigh. Luke 21:28

- ἀπολύτρωσις *apolutrosis*
  a releasing effected by payment of ransom
- "redemption" 9X:

Luke 21:28	Rom 3:24	Rom 8:23
1Cor 1:30	Eph 1:7	Eph 1:14
Eph 4:30	Col 1:14	Heb 9:15

Then when you see

The Beginning of Sorrows

	Matthew	Luke	Revelation
• False Christs	24:4-5	21:4	6:1-2
• Wars	24:6	21:9,10	6:3-4
• Famines	24:7a	21:11	6:5-6
• Pestilences	24:7b-8	21:12	6:7-8
• Earthquakes	24:9	21:24	6:12
Cosmic Upheaval	24:10-13	21:25	6:12-17

Different Emphasis?

- "But *before* all these..." Luke 21:12
  [False Christs, Wars, Famines, Earthquakes]
- "All these are the beginning of sorrows."
- "*Then* shall they..." Matthew 24:8,9

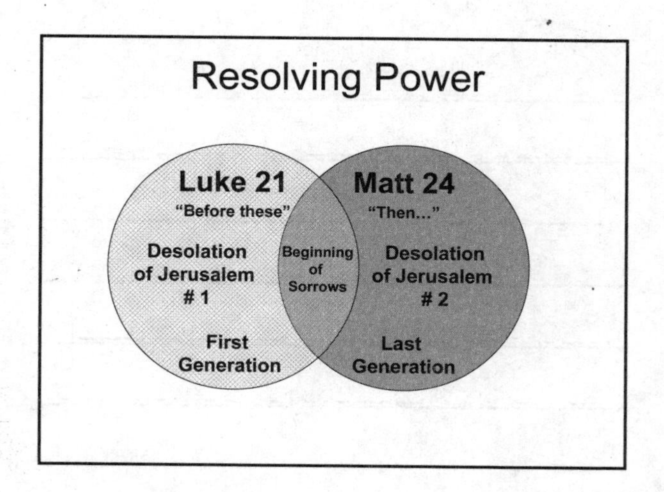

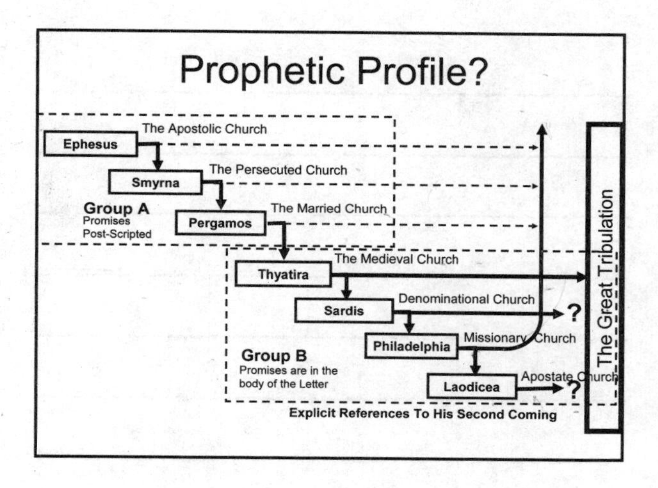

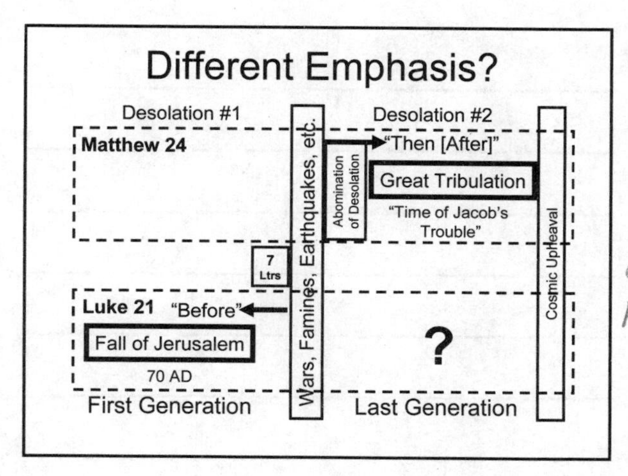

Jesus
people in daytime
privatly to 4 at night

Luke
publically
in Temple to Gentiles

Distinctions

- Matthew
  - To the Jews
  - Private Briefing on the Mt. of Olives

  Matt 24:3; Mark 13:3
- Luke
  - To the Gentiles
  - In the Temple Luke 21:37,38

to believers

Not the same account

Faithful remnant fled
no Christians lost their lives

In Conclusion

- Eschatology
  - Abomination of Desolation: "stand in the holy place"
    - Antiochus Epiphanes
    - Caligula & Petronius
  - The Hiatus of the Seige in 70 AD
- Additional Implications
  - Deity of Christ

Issues

- The Destruction of Jerusalem
  - in 70 AD? Or is it yet future?
- The "Abomination of Desolation"?
  - What is it?
  - When did it happen? Or has it yet?
- The Great Tribulation
- The Parable of the Fig Tree
- (Which) "Generation shall not pass away"?
- * The Doctrine of Imminence
  - For each of us individually…

MATTHEW - SESSION 18: Chapter 24 -- Part 2

Luke 21

1) List the differences between Matthew 24 and Luke 21: the occasion, the audiences, and the emphasis.

2) Diagram both, showing the common elements and the distinctives. (Include the 7 letters of Revelation 2 & 3.)

3) Has the destruction of Jerusalem detailed in the Luke's account happened yet?

4) When Nero died, who succeeded him? How does this impact our understanding of Luke 21?

5) In the fall of Jerusalem in 70 AD: a) How many Jews died? b) How many Christians?

Preparation for the Next Session:

Study Matthew 25.

Group Discussion Questions: See the *Small Group Leaders* section of this workbook.

Session 19

The Gospel of

Matthew

Chapter 25

Unit II:

The Judean Ministry & The Final Week

Matthew 19 - 28

The Final Week

	Matthew	Mark	Luke	John
Triumphal Entry	21	11	19	12
	22, 23	12	20	
Olivet Discourse	24, 25	13	21	
Last Seder	26	14	22	13-18
Crucifixion	27	15	23	19
Resurrection	28	16	24	20,21

Matthew 25

- The Ten Virgins
- The Ten Talents
- The "Sheep & Goat" Judgment

oil represents H.S.

Then shall the kingdom of heaven be likened unto ten virgins, which took their lamps, and went forth to meet the bridegroom.
And five of them were wise, and five *were* foolish.
They that *were* foolish took their lamps, and took no oil with them:
But the wise took oil in their vessels with their lamps.

Matthew 25:1-4

Afterward came also the other virgins, saying, Lord, Lord, open to us.
But he answered and said, Verily I say unto you, I know you not.
Watch therefore, for ye know neither the day nor the hour wherein the Son of man cometh.

Matthew 25:11-13

οἶδα *oida* intimate, experiential type of knowledge

The Virgins

- They were set apart, called to give light!
- Five of them had their profession empty (the wick will burn for awhile without oil). They had no oil.
- Oil is a symbol of the Holy Spirit.
- No evidence that they are saved.
- How do we know they were not saved?

The Virgins

- They were ***outside*** when the door was shut.
  - Also, when they asked the Lord to open the door, He said, "I know you not."!
- The scary part of this is that they *thought* they were saved.
- Is the Holy Spirit in your life?

For the kingdom of heaven is as a man travelling into a far country, who called his own servants, and delivered unto them his goods.

And unto one he gave five talents, to another two, and to another one; to every man according to his several ability; and straightway took his journey.

Matthew 25:14,15

Take therefore the talent from him, and give *it* unto him which hath ten talents.

For unto every one that hath shall be given, and he shall have abundance: but from him that hath not shall be taken away even that which he hath.

And cast ye the unprofitable servant into outer darkness: there shall be weeping and gnashing of teeth.

Matthew 25:28-30

"Talents"?

- They are generally treated as gifts (as in skills).
- These talents are opportunities, and we will be held accountable.
- Hiding them for safekeeping is not using them.
  - Whatever resources the Lord has put at your disposal (money, influence, skills)
- What are ***you*** doing with them?
  - You lose when you don't put them to use…

Talents represent a year's wage - in this parable - talent is opportunity to share

gifts

The Three Judgments

1. The Sheep & Goat Judgment
   - Judgment of the Nations
2. The Bema Seat of Christ
   - The Believer's Rewards
3. The Great White Throne Judgment
   - The Final Judgment

And the King shall answer and say unto them, Verily I say unto you, Inasmuch as ye have done *it* unto one of the least of these my brethren, ye have done *it* unto me.
Matthew 25:40

- *Three* groups of people here:
  - the Sheep
  - the Goats
  - the Brethren

Then shall he say also unto them on the left hand, Depart from me, ye cursed, into everlasting fire, prepared for the devil and his angels:
For I was an hungred, and ye gave me no meat: I was thirsty, and ye gave me no drink:
I was a stranger, and ye took me not in: naked, and ye clothed me not: sick, and in prison, and ye visited me not.
Matthew 25:41-43

The Sheep & the Goats

→ mercy seat

- This is *not* a resurrection judgment. There are four groups of people that go into *Gehenna*, or the outer darkness:
  - The Devil's Pair: the beast and the false prophet
  - The unrighteous Gentiles (this judgment)
  - (At the end of the millennium): the Devil and his angels, and finally
  - The wicked dead from the Great White Throne judgment
- Here *Gentile individuals* are being judged
- And they are judged in such a way that even the winners are puzzled…

The "Brethren"?

- Some consider all believers as this group
- Perhaps a more specific application:
  - The Jewish remnant which will be given the mandate to be His witness throughout the world
  - The "Great Tribulation" ("Time of Jacob's Trouble"), focusing on Israel and specifically the 144,000: His ministers proclaiming the gospel
  - They will be under great persecution
  - Certain people will choose to protect them, feed them, hide them, etc.

The "Brethren"?

- We can also see a historical application of this perspective:
  - Studies that have been published which show how nations rise and fall in relation to their treatment of the Jews
    - The Babylonians vs. the Persians
    - The Inquisition and the Armada
    - The British Empire
    - Nazi Germany
- This particular application, however, is yet future.

The Final Week

	Matthew	Mark	Luke	John
Triumphal Entry	21	11	19	12
	22 23	12	20	
Olivet Discourse	24 25	13	21	
Last Seder	26	14	22	13-18
Crucifixion	27	15	23	19
Resurrection	28	16	24	20,21

MATTHEW- SESSION 19: Chapter 25

1) Summarize the ancient Jewish wedding ceremony as an eschatological type.

2) Which of the ten virgins were saved and which ones were not? How do we know?

3) What was wrong with the steward who avoided risk and sought safety?

4) Contrast the following three "judgments": Who is involved; and what are the consequences?
   1) The Sheep and Goat
   2) The Bema Seat
   3) The Great White Throne

Preparation for the Next Session:

Read Matthew 26, Mark 14, Luke 22, and John 13 – 17.

Group Discussion Questions: See the *Small Group Leaders* section of this workbook.

Session 20

The Gospel of

Matthew

Chapter 26
The Last Seder

Matthew 26

- At Bethany 1-16
  - Worship vs Waste
- In the Upper Room 17-30
  - Faithfulness vs Betrayal
- Gethsemane 31-56
  - Submission vs Resistance

Matthew 26

1.	Prediction of His suffering and death	1-5
2.	His anointing at Bethany	6-13
3.	Judas' betrayal	14-16
4.	The Passover meal	17-25
5.	The institution of the Lord's supper	26-35
6.	The Garden of Gethesmane	36-46
7.	His arrest and accusations	47-68
8.	The denial of Peter	69-75

Three times in a year shall all thy males appear before the LORD thy God in the place which he shall choose; in the feast of unleavened bread, and in the feast of weeks, and in the feast of tabernacles: and they shall not appear before the LORD empty:

Deuteronomy 16:16

Gifts at His Birth

- Not necessarily all mentioned These mentioned because they are prophetic:
  - Gold - deity
  - Frankincense - priesthood (mixed into the shewbread by the priests)
  - Myrrh – when crushed, an ointment for burial
- Prophet, Priest, and King

Always Misunderstood

- Her sister Martha misunderstood her when Mary sat at Jesus' feet to hear Him teach the Word Luke 10:38-42
- Judas and the other disciples misunderstood her when she anointed Jesus Matt 26:8,9
- Her friends and neighbors misunderstood her when she came out of the house to meet Jesus after Lazarus had been buried John 11:28–31

And I said unto them, If ye think good, give *me* my price; and if not, forbear. So they weighed for my price thirty *pieces* of silver.

And the LORD said unto me, Cast it unto the potter: a goodly price that I was prised at of them. And I took the thirty *pieces* of silver, and cast them to the potter in the house of the LORD.

Zechariah 11:12,13

Passover

- The *Akedah* Gen 22:7
  - "God will provide Himself a lamb"
- John's Introduction (2X):
  - "Behold the Lamb that taketh away the sin of the world" John 1:29, 36
- Anticipatory Symbolisms:
  - Leaven, Not a bone broken, et al…
- Timing Gen 8:4
  - Anniversary of Noah's New Beginning

Time Dimension Paradox:

Fate vs Free Will

- From the divine point of view, *from outside the Time Dimension,* Judas' treachery was predicted in Scripture and was included in the plan of God.
- From the human point of view, *from within the Time Dimension,* Judas was guilty of a base crime and was completely responsible for what he did.

Who's in Control Here?

- "Not on a feast day?" Matt 26:5
  - This is the biggest of them all!
  - 1 of 3 that were compulsory Deut 16:16
- Judas now had to "fish or cut bait"
- Arrangements needed to made:
  - With the High Priest
  - To muster the troops
  - Morning appointment with Pilate

Bread and Wine

- Melchizedek Gen 14:18
- Joseph's Prophetic Interpretations
  - Wine Steward Gen 40:10f
  - Baker Gen 40:16f
- Bread of Life John 6:35f
- Wine at Cana John 2:6f

Four Cups of Passover

Exodus 6:6,7

1. The cup of the Bringing Out
2. The cup of the Delivery
3. The cup of Redemption or Blessing*
4. The cup of the Taking Out

1 Corinthians 10:16

After two days was *the feast of* the passover, and of unleavened bread: and the chief priests and the scribes sought how they might take him by craft, and put *him* to death.
But they said, Not on the feast *day*, lest there be an uproar of the people.

Mark 14:1,2

And the first day of unleavened bread, when they killed the passover, his disciples said unto him, Where wilt thou that we go and prepare that thou mayest eat the passover?
And he sendeth forth two of his disciples, and saith unto them, Go ye into the city, and there shall meet you a man bearing a pitcher of water: follow him.

Mark 14:12,13

The Son of man indeed goeth, as it is written of him: but woe to that man by whom the Son of man is betrayed! good were it for that man if he had never been born.

Mark 14:21

Ahithophel

At Absalom's revolt Ahithophel deserted David Ps 41:9; 55:12-14
and espoused the cause of Absalom 2 Sam 15:12

David sent his old friend, Hushai, back to Absalom, in order that he might counteract the counsel of Ahithophel 2 Sam 15:31-37

Ahithophel

This end was so far gained that Ahithophel saw he had no longer any influence, and accordingly he at once left the camp of Absalom and returned to Giloh, his native place, where, after arranging his worldly affairs, he hanged himself, and was buried in the sepulchre of his fathers. 2 Sam 17:1-23

He was the type of Judas. Ps 41:9

And as they did eat, Jesus took bread, and blessed, and brake it, and gave to them, and said, Take, eat: this is my body.

And he took the cup, and when he had given thanks, he gave it to them: and they all drank of it.

And he said unto them, This is my blood of the new testament, which is shed for many.
Mark 14:22-24

MATTHEW- SESSION 20: Chapter 26 -- Part 1

The Last Seder

1) List the principle symbolisms of the Passover that were fulfilled in Jesus Christ.

2) Who established the *timing* of the events of the evening of the Last Supper?

3) Was Judas responsible for having fulfilled prophecy? In what ways was Ahithophel a type of Judas? Why did Ahithophel betray David?

4) What are the four cups at Passover based upon?

Preparation for the Next Session:

Read John 13 – 17.

Group Discussion Questions: See the *Small Group Leaders* section of this workbook.

Session 21

The Gospel of

Matthew

Upper Room Discourse
John 13 - 17

Foot Washing

1) Example of humility Jn 13:14
2) Rebuke to pride Lk 22:24-27
3) Picture of our daily cleansing Jn 13:10
4) Warning to Judas Iscariot Jn 13:18
5) Picture of His humiliation Phil 2:5-11
6) Reminder of His union and communion with the believer Jn 13:8

Glorified

1) Greatest event in the universe
2) Reversed the conduct of the first man
3) Through death destroyed him who had the power of death: the Devil Heb 2:14
4) Purchased for Himself the entire elect of God.

   What held Him to the Cross?
   Not the nails: the strength of His love.

5) Glorified man at God's right hand. Jn 17:22; Phil 2:9-11

Four Questions

1) Lord, Where Are You Going?
13:33, 36; 14:1

- Jesus will soon be invisible to them, yet He wants them to rejoice. 1 Pet 1:8

The Blessed Hope

1) Many mansions
2) He will return for us: [the "*Harpazo*"]
3) New thing: a *man* in heaven!

Redemption of the purchased possession, in heaven, by better sacrifices Heb 9:23; Eph 1:14; Col 1:20

The Marriage Fulfilled

- Covenant established: 1 Cor 11:25
- Purchase price: 1 Cor 6:19-20
- Bride set apart: Eph 5:25-27; 1 Cor 1:2; 6:11; Heb 10:10; 13:12
- Reminded of the covenant: 1 Cor 11:25-26
- Bridegroom left for the Father's house…
- Escort to accompany Him upon His return to gather His Bride 1 Thess4:16-17

The Way

- *hodos:* road, highway.
  - The highway to heaven
    7X: John 14:6; Acts 9:2; 19:9,23; 22:4; 24:14,22)
- This phrase speaks of the exclusiveness of Christ
  Acts 4:12; 1 Cor 3:11; 1 Tim 2:6
  - Also in Gethsemane, 3X...
- [Cf. The word "Zodiac" is from the Sanskrit *sodi* "the way"] *Mazzeroth* Ps 19

The Truth

- "Truth": Spirit of (the) Truth *had not yet been given* Jn 16:13; cf. 1 Cor 2:10,11
- Pilate: "What is truth?"
  Jn 18:38; Eph 4:18; Ecc 7:29; Rom 3:11; Col 2:3

The Life

- Prodigal Son: "dead, and is alive again" Lk 15:24; Jn 3:36; 5:24
- Adam, before sin, enjoyed communion with his Maker; he knew Him; and he possessed spiritual life.
  - In "the day thou eatest..."
  - Adam had a threefold need:
    - reconciliation
    - illumination
    - regeneration

Four Questions

1: Lord, Where Are You Going? 14:1
2: How Can We Know the Way? 14:5-7
3: Show Us the Father 14:8-21
4: How Can You Manifest Yourself to Us and Not to the World? 14:22-31

"Taketh away"?

1) The true believer apostatizing?
   - Armenians: The Christian who does not abide in Christ loses his salvation
   - Seems to be refuted by Jn 4:14; 10:28; 18:9; Rom 5:9-10; 8:35-39

2) Eternal security position: A mere professor, never truly united to Christ;
   - But were they *branches?* v.5; "in me"...

"Taketh away"?

3) Fruit bearing, not salvation 2 Pet 1:5-7, 8; Tit 3:14

4) *Airei,* "taketh away." The root for "resurrection": "to take up," "lift up"
   - Cf. Lk 17:13; Acts 4:24; Jn 11:41; Rev 10:5
     – Fruitbearing: The vinedresser does not cut away a vine, but gently lifts it up to the sun so it has an opportunity to bear fruit. Not judgment but *encouragement* is referenced here cf. Dan 7:4

Various Views

1) Loss of salvation?
2) Presumption; profession without salvation
3) Believer losing his reward
4) Premature death of the non-abider; Stripped of gifts Mt 5:13; Lk 8:18; 2 Jn 8
   - Ananias and Sapphira Acts 5:1-11
   - Sin at the Lord's table 1 Cor 11:28-30
   - Sin unto death 1 Jn 5:16

The Importance of Prayer

- During His baptism Lk 3:21
- At the commencement of public ministry Mk 1:35
- The eve of selecting disciples Lk 6:12 (all night long)
- At the Transfiguration Lk 9:29
- When He ceased to breathe Lk 23:46
- *Our most important work is prayer!*

All Factors of Redemption

1. Salvation 17:2
2. Manifestation 17:6
3. Representation 17:9
4. Preservation 17:12
5. Sanctification 17:17-19
6. Identification 17:21
7. Glorification 17:22

Seven Specific Requests

1. Glorification of the Son 1
2. Restoration of His original glory 5
3. Protection of His disciples (and future believers) 11,15
4. Sanctification 17
5. Unification 21-23
6. Glorification 24
7. That the world would know 21

Relationship with the World

- We have a different standing:
  - in Christ, not Adam.
- We have a different nature:
  - born of the spirit, not the flesh.
- We have a different Master:
  - not of the god of this world.
- We have a different aim:
  - to glorify God, not self.

"Same as" in John 17

The believer has

1. the same **life** as Christ 17:2
2. the same **security** as Christ 17:11
3. the same **separation** as Christ 17:14
4. the same **sending** into the world as Christ 17:18
5. the same **union** as Christ 17:21
6. the same **glory** as Christ 17:22
7. the same **love** as Christ 17:23

MATTHEW- SESSION 21:

John 13 ± 18: The Upper Room Discourse

1) Why is this passage called the "job description of the Holy Spirit"?

2) Explain the primary lessons (6?) of the foot-washing event in the Upper Room. Contrast this with Nicolaitanism.

3) How is "loving one another" a ™*New*∫ commandment? How is this different than Leviticus 19:18?

4) What were the four questions posed and their answers?

5) List the ways that the ancient Jewish wedding ceremony had eschatological significance.

6) Where was the *Harpazo* introduced in the Gospels? Where is it explained in the epistles?

7) “And when [the Holy Spirit] is come, He will reprove the world of sin, and of righteousness, and of judgment” (John 16:8). Explain the three “reproves.”

8) Outline the Lord’s Prayer in John 17.

9) Who does God love, yet did *not* pray for?

10) Which prayer of Moses, Elijah, and Jonah was *not* granted?

Preparation for the Next Session:

The Night of Nights:	Gethsemane	Matthew 26:36-56 Mark 14:33-52 Luke 22:40-54 John 18:1-13
The Jewish Trials		Matthew 26:57-75 Mark 14:53-72 Luke 22:55-71 John 18:14-29

Group Discussion Questions: See the *Small Group Leaders* section of this workbook.

Session 22

The Gospel of

Matthew

Matthew 26

Gethsemane

Jewish Trials

Matthew 26

1.	Prediction of His suffering and death	1-5
2.	His anointing at Bethany	6-13
3.	Judas' betrayal	14-16
4.	The Passover meal	17-25
5.	The institution of the Lord's supper	26-35
6.	The Garden of Gethsemane	36-46
7.	His arrest and accusations	47-68
8.	The denial of Peter	69-75

Session 22

- The Night of Nights
  - Gethsemane — Matt 26:36-56, Mark 14:33-52, Luke 22:40-54, John 18:1-13
  - The Jewish Trials — Matt 26:57-75, Mark 14:53-72, Luke 22:55-71, John 18:14-29

Cups

"The cup which my Father hath given me."

• Cup pass from me	Mt 26:39
• Cup of Salvation	Ps 116:3
• Cup of Tribulation	Ps 11:6; Jer 25:15 cf. Ps 75:8

And Jesus saith unto them, All ye shall be offended because of me this night: for it is written, I will smite the shepherd, and the sheep shall be scattered.

But after that I am risen, I will go before you into Galilee.

But Peter said unto him, Although all shall be offended, yet *will* not I.

Mark 14:27-29

Summary

- Jesus' death was no accident.
  - Jesus' words at the Last Supper make no sense at all if Jesus was not master of His own death.
  - Jesus maintained sovereign, premeditated, precise mastery.
- *A God who is control when the foundations of His own earthly existence are crumbling is a God who can be trusted to sustain us when it appears our life is tumbling in.*

And when he was at the place, he said unto them, Pray that ye enter not into temptation.

And he was withdrawn from them about a stone's cast, and kneeled down, and prayed,

Saying, Father, if thou be willing, remove this cup from me: nevertheless not my will, but thine, be done.

And there appeared an angel unto him from heaven, strengthening him.

Luke 22:40-43

Six Trials

- Jewish Trials:
  - Before Annas — John 18:12–14
  - Before Caiaphas — Matt. 26:57–68
  - Before the Sanhedrin — Matt. 27:1–2
- Roman Trials:
  - Before Pilate — John 18:28–38
  - Before Herod — Luke 23:6–12
  - Before Pilate — John 18:39–19:16

- Self-incrimination was prohibited in their law.
- Virtually all of the aspects of the six trials Jesus endured were illegally administered.
- The religious trial was over. The next step was the criminal trial before the civil authorities.
  - Only they could execute Him for death.
  - *By a method that had been invented only a century earlier; yet prophesied 800 years earlier!*

The Sceptre Departs

- Archelaus was the 2nd son of Herod the Great
  - (The older son, Herod Antipater, was murdered by Herod the Great, along with other family members.) Josephus, *Antiquities,* 17:13
  - Archelaus' mother was a Samaritan (1/4 or less of Jewish blood) and was never accepted
- After the death of Herod (4 B.C.?), Archelaus had been placed over Judea as "Entharch" by Caesar Augustus
- Broadly rejected, he was dethroned and banished in 6-7 A.D

When Jesus had spoken these words, he went forth with his disciples over the brook Cedron, where was a garden, into the which he entered, and his disciples.

And Judas also, which betrayed him, knew the place: for Jesus ofttimes resorted thither with his disciples.

Judas then, having received a band of men and officers from the chief priests and Pharisees, cometh thither with lanterns and torches and weapons.

John 18:1-3

Two Gardens

All was delightful;

All was terrible.

Adam and Eve parleyed with Satan;

Last Adam sought face of His Father.

Adam sinned;

Savior suffered.

Adam fell;

Redeemer conquered.

Lessons from Peter

- The danger of self-confidence
- The consequences of prayerlessness (Could he not watch for one hour?)
- The perils of companionship with the wicked
- The influence of the fear of man

  The fear of man bringeth a snare: but whoso putteth his trust in the LORD shall be safe

  Pro 29:25

Legal Irregularities

- The binding of a prisoner before he was condemned was unlawful unless resistance was offered or expected. Jesus offered none. John 18:12,24
- It was illegal for judges to participate in the arrest of the accused. John 18:3
- No legal transactions, including a trial, could be conducted at night. John 18:28

Legal Irregularities

- The arrest was affected through the agency of an informer and a traitor.

  John 18:5; Ex 23:6-8
- While an acquittal could be pronounced the same day, any other verdict required a majority of two and had to come on a subsequent day.

  Matt 26:65,66
- No prisoner could be convicted on his own evidence. Matt 26:63-65

Legal Irregularities

- It was the duty of a judge to see that the interest of the accused was fully protected. John 18:14
- Preliminary hearings before a magistrate were completely foreign to the Jewish legal system. John 18:13
- The judges sought false witnesses against Jesus. Matt 26:59; Mark 14:56

Legal Irregularities

- In a Jewish court the accused was to be assumed innocent until proved guilty by two or more witnesses. Matt 18:63
- The Jews failed to find two witnesses agreeing against Jesus. Mark 14:59
- When the witnesses first disagreed, the prisoner should have been released. Mark 14:56-59

Legal Irregularities

- The trial under Caiaphas took place in his home rather than the council chamber where it should have been held. John 18:13-16
- The Court lacked the civil authority to condemn a man to death. John 18:31
- It was illegal to conduct a session of the court on a feast day. John 18:28

MATTHEW- SESSION 22: Chapter 26 -- Part 2

1) What critical doctrine is exemplified in Christ's prayer in Gethsemane?

2) What are the other lessons of Gethsemane?

3) How dangerous are angels? Explain, with examples.

4) Did Jesus really claim to be God? When, where, and under what conditions?

5) Summarize the illegalities in the trials of Jesus.

Preparation for the Next Session:

Read The Crucifixion: Matthew 27
Mark 15
Luke 23
John 18

also: Psalm 22 and Isaiah 53

Group Discussion Questions: See the *Small Group Leaders* section of this workbook.

Session 23

The Gospel of

Matthew

Chapter 27
The Crucifixion

Pontius Pilate

- Ruled Judea in a reckless and arbitrary fashion.
- In AD 36, he was deposed by Vitellius and sent to Rome, tried under Caligula. Tradition: Pilate killed himself.

  Josephus, *Ant.* 18:4, sec 1,2;

  Eusebius, *Historia Ecclesiastica, II,* ii. 7
- The Coptic church came to believe that he became a Christian.

Pilate's Interviews

	Outside:	Inside:
1.	John 18:28-32;	
2.		John 18:33-37
3.	John 18:38-40	
4.		John 19:1-3
5.	John 19:4-7	
6.		John 19:8-11
7.	John 19:12-46	

Pilate's Attempts to Release

1.	"You judge Him"	John 18:31
2.	"He is innocent"	John 18:38
3.	Jews substitute Barabbas	John 18:39
4.	Partial punishment	John 19:1
5.	Play on pity	John 19:5
6.	"Behold your King"	John 19:14

Mutual Exchange of Positions

- Barabbas is installed in all the rights and privileges of Jesus Christ
- while the latter enters upon all the infamy and horror of the rebel's position
- The delinquent's guilt and cross become the lot of the Just One
- all the civil rights and immunities of the later are now the property of the delinquent.

Pilate therefore went forth again, and saith unto them, Behold, I bring him forth to you, that ye may know that I find no fault in him.

Then came Jesus forth, wearing the crown of thorns, and the purple robe. And Pilate saith unto them, Behold the man!

When the chief priests therefore and officers saw him, they cried out, saying, Crucify him, crucify him. Pilate saith unto them, Take ye him, and crucify him: for I find no fault in him.

John 19:4-6

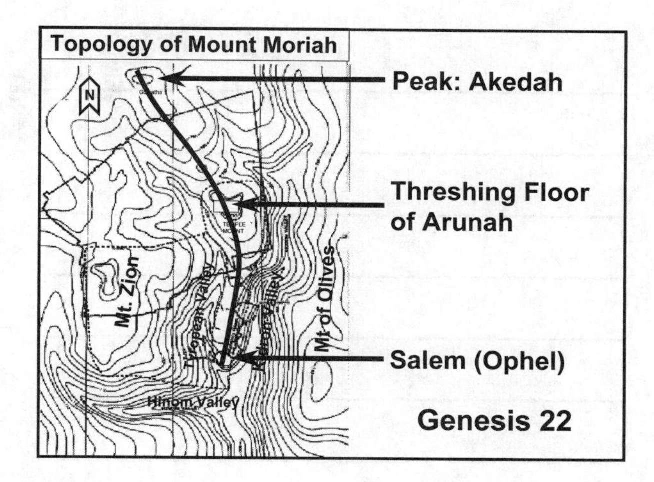

Levitical Locations

- On the north side
  - Burnt Offerings Lev 1:11
  - Sin Offerings Lev 6:25
- Outside the camp Lev 4:12, 21; 16:27
- " Without the gate" Heb 13:12

And Pilate wrote a title, and put *it* on the cross. And the writing was,

JESUS OF NAZARETH
THE KING OF THE JEWS.

This title then read many of the Jews: for the place where Jesus was crucified was nigh to the city: and it was written in Hebrew, *and* Greek, *and* Latin.

John 19:19,20

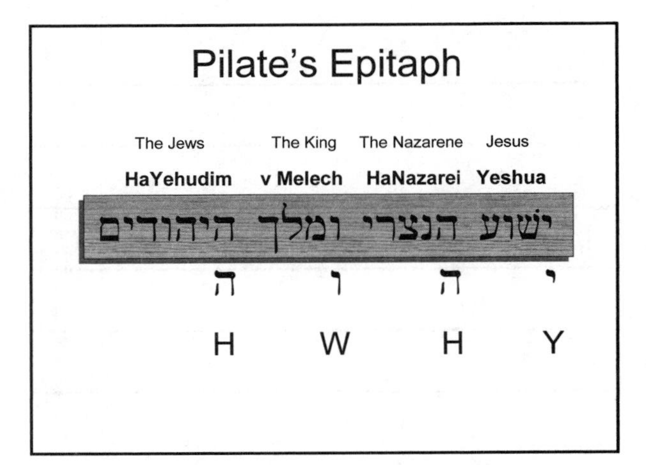

My God, my God, why hast thou forsaken me? *why art thou so* far from helping me, *and from* the words of my roaring?

O my God, I cry in the daytime, but thou hearest not; and in the night season, and am not silent.

But thou *art* holy, *O thou* that inhabitest the praises of Israel.

Psalm 22:1-3

And after this Joseph of Arimathaea, being a disciple of Jesus, but secretly for fear of the Jews, besought Pilate that he might take away the body of Jesus: and Pilate gave *him* leave. He came therefore, and took the body of Jesus.

John 19:38

κεκρυμμένος δὲ διὰ τὸν φόβον τῶν ʼιουδαίων
κεκρυμμένως

"Secreted," not "secretly" : It is an adjective, not an adverb.

Who hath believed our report? and to whom is the arm of the LORD revealed?

For he shall grow up before him as a tender plant, and as a root out of a dry ground: he hath no form nor comeliness; and when we shall see him, *there is* no beauty that we should desire him.

He is despised and rejected of men; a man of sorrows, and acquainted with grief: and we hid as it were *our* faces from him; he was despised, and we esteemed him not.

Isaiah 53:1-3

Yet it pleased the LORD to bruise him; he hath put *him* to grief: when thou shalt make his soul an offering for sin, he shall see *his* seed, he shall prolong *his* days, and the pleasure of the LORD shall prosper in his hand.

He shall see of the travail of his soul, *and* shall be satisfied: by his knowledge shall my righteous servant justify many; for he shall bear their iniquities.

Isaiah 53:10,11

Summary of Events

1) Jesus arrived at Golgatha
   Matt 27:33; Mark 15:22; Luke 23:33; John 19:17
2) He refused the offer of wine, vinegar and myrrh
   Matt 27:34; Mark 15:23
3) Nailed to the cross between 2 thieves
   Matt 27:35-38; Mark 15:24-28; Luke 23:33-38; John 19:18;
4) 1st cry from Cross: "Father forgive them for they know not what they do"
   Luke 23:34

7 Cries from the Cross

1) "Father, forgive them for they know not what they do." Luke 23:34
2) "Today shalt thou be with Me in paradise." Luke 23:43
3) "Woman, Behold thy Son! Behold thy mother!" John 19:26-27
4) My God, My God, Why hast Thou forsaken me?" Psalm 22:1
5) "I thirst." John 19:28. Cf. Ps 69:21
6) "It is finished." *Tetelestai*! Paid in full John 19:30
7) "Father, into Thy hands I commit My spirit." Luke 23:46

Order of events

1. Jesus arrived at Golgatha Ma 27:33; Mk 15:22;Lu 23:33;Jo 19:17
2. He refused the offer of wine, vinegar and myrrh Ma 27:34; Mk 15:23
3. Nailed to the cross between 2 thieves Ma 27:35-38; Mk 15:24-28; Lu 23:33-38; Jo 19:18;
4. 1st cry from Cross: Father forgive them for they know not… Luk 23:34
5. Garments allocated Ma 27:35; Mk 15:24; Luk 23:34;Jo 19:23
6. Jews mocked Jesus Ma 27:39-43; Mk 15:29-32; Lk 23:35-37
7. Conversed with two thieves Lu 23:39-43
8. 2nd Cry: "you will be with me in paradise" Lu 23:43
9. 3rd cry: "Woman, behold your son" Jo 19:26-27
10. Darkness, noon to 3 PM Ma 27:45; Mk 15:33; Lu 23:44
11. 4th Cry: "My God…"Ma 27:46,47; Mk 15:34-36
12. 5th Cry: "I am thirsty" Jo 19:28
13. He drank wine vinegar Jo 19:29
14. 6th cry: "It is finished" Jo 19:30
15. Drank vine vinegar from sponge Ma 27:48; Mk 15:36
16. 7th cry: "Father, into your hands…" Luk 23:46
17. He dismissed His Spirit Ma 27:50; Mk 15:37;Lu 23:46; Jo 19:30
18. Temple curtain torn in two Ma 27:51; Mk 15:38; Luk 23:45
19. Roman soldiers declare,"surely He was…" Ma 27:54;Mk 15:39

- 1. Carrying His cross Jn 19:17
- 2. Simon substituted Lk 23:26
- 3. Offer of stupefying drink Mt 27:34
- 4. Nailed between two thieves Jn 19:18-24
- 5. "Father, forgive them" [City of Refuge...] Lk 23:34
- 6. Jews mock Jesus Mt 27:39-43
- 7. One thief rails at Jesus; the other receives salvation Lk 23:39-43
- 8. "Today shalt thou be with me" Lk 23:43
- 9. "Woman, Behold thy son" Jn 19:26,27
- 10. Darkness Mt 27:45
- 11. "My God..." Mt 27:46
- 12. "I Thirst" Jn 19:28
- 13. "It is finished" Jn 19:30
- 14. "Father, into thy hands..." Lk 23:46
- 15. Our Lord dismisses His spirit Jn 19:30

MATTHEW- SESSION 23: Chapter 27

The Crucifixion

1) When, and under what conditions, did the Jewish leadership lose the right to capital punishment?

2) What happened to the 30 pieces of silver that Judas received? Why is that prophetically significant?

3) List the ways in which Jesus and Barabbas exchanged places.

4) Explain the discrepancies between the purchase of the threshing floor by David in 2 Samuel 24:18-24 and 1 Chronicles 21:25. Was Ornan and Araunah the same or were there two incidents?

5) All burnt and sin offerings were to be on which side of the Camp? Give references. Where was Christ crucified?

6) List the passages in the Old Testament that expressly indicate that the Messiah would be executed.

7) List the prophetic details included in Psalm 22.

8) List the prophetic details included in Isaiah 53 (beginning at 52:14).

9) How many soldiers were there at the foot of the cross?

Preparation for the Next Session:

Read:
Matthew 28
Mark 16
Luke 24
John 20 & 21

and also:
1 Corinthians 15

Group Discussion Questions: See the *Small Group Leaders* section of this workbook.

Session 24

The Gospel of

Matthew

Resurrection

Final Session:

The Resurrection

Matt 28
Mark 16
Luke 24
John 20,21

also

1 Corinthians 15

And *one* shall say unto him, What *are* these wounds in thine hands? Then he shall answer, *Those* with which I was wounded *in* the house of my friends.

Zechariah 13:6

153 Fishes?

- ὀψάριον *opsarion*
  - Implies used for food
  - Only in John: 6:9,11; 21:9,10,13
- ἰχθύς *ichthus*
  - Does not signify purpose of the fish
  - 3X: John 21:6,8,11
- A *Remez*?

Fishers of Men?

- Their net was effectual (didn't break)
- Each was counted
- All were "great" (*megas*)
- None were lost

He saith unto him the third time, Simon, *son* of Jonas, lovest thou me? Peter was grieved because he said unto him the third time, Lovest thou me? And he said unto him, Lord, thou knowest all things; thou knowest that I love thee. Jesus saith unto him, Feed my sheep.

John 21:17

ἀγαπάω *agapeo* *to love, wholly committed*

φιλέω *phileo* *to be fond of, befriend*

Sunday Morning

- Three women, Mary Magdalene, and Mary the mother of James, and Salome, start for the sepulchre, followed by other women bearing spices.
  - The three find the stone rolled away, and Mary Magdalene goes to tell the disciples. **Luke 23:55–24:9; John 20:1, 2**
  - Mary, the mother of James and Joses, draws nearer the tomb and sees the angel of the Lord. **Matt. 28:2**
  - She goes back to meet the other women following with the spices.

Subsequent Appearances

- Two on Emmaus Rd, Sun PM Luke 24:13-32
- Peter, sometime that day Luke 24:34
- Ten, that night (w/o Thomas) Luke 24:36ff
- Eleven, 8 days later (w/ Thomas) John 20:26-31
- Seven, Galilean breakfast John 21:9-14
- Eleven, in Galilee Matt 28:16-20
- 500, in Galilee 1 Cor 15:6
- James in Jerusalem 1 Cor 15:7
- Many at the Ascension Luke 24:44f

Significance of the Resurrection

1) Proves that Jesus is God's Son John 10:17–18
2) Verifies the truth of Scripture Psa 16:10; 110:1
3) Assures our own future resurrection 1 Thes. 4:13–18
4) Proof of a future judgment Acts 17:31
5) Basis for Christ's heavenly priesthood Heb. 7:23–28
6) Gives power for Christian living Rom. 6:4
7) Assures our future inheritance 1 Peter 1:3–5.

The Gospel Defined

For I delivered unto you first of all that which I also received, how that Christ died for our sins according to the scriptures;
And that he was buried, and that he rose again the third day according to the scriptures:
1 Corinthians 15:3,4

Last 12 verses of Mark?

- Doubt generated by the Alexandrian Codices:
  - "Added later"?
  - Role of Westcott & Hort
- Expurgated by the Gnostics
  - Quoted by Ireneaus, Hipplatus, et al
- Authentication by heptadic structures
  - Over 35 heptadic constraints
  - Defy replication, *even with computer assistance!*

A Lingering Mystery:

Why did they all seem to have trouble recognizing Him after His resurrection?

Why Wasn't He Recognized?

- By Mary in the Garden? John 20:11-16
- On the Emmaus Road? Luke 24:13-32
- In the Upper Room? Luke 24:33-43
- By the Sea of Galilee? John 21:3-12

An Enigmatic Remark

Jesus saith unto them, Come and dine. And none of the disciples durst ask him, Who art thou? knowing that it was the Lord.

John 21:12

As many were astonished at thee; His visage was so marred more than any man, and His form more than the sons of men:

Isaiah 52:14,15

"so marred from the form of man was His aspect that His appearance was not that of a son of man."

Old Testament Descriptions

- Psalm 22
- Isaiah 53
- Isaiah 50:6
- Zechariah 12:10
- Revelation 5:6

of Jesus' on the cross

The Boundaries of "Reality"

The Metacosm

Finite Limits: *Digital Simulation*

The Microcosm

(Indivisible Units)

Quantum Physics
Subatomic particles

The Macrocosm

(Finite)

Astronomy
Astrophysics

Size

That Christ may dwell in your hearts by faith; that ye, being rooted and grounded in love, May be able to comprehend with all saints what is the breadth, and length, and depth, and height; And to know the love of Christ, which passeth knowledge, that ye might be filled with all the fulness of God.

Ephesians 3:17-19

Four Dimensions!

MATTHEW- SESSION 24: Chapter 28

The Resurrection

1) How did Andrew Bonar profile the details of the sepulcher over 40 years *before* the Garden Tomb was discovered?

2) List the events, in order, that fateful Sunday morning.

3) On which day of the week did the Crucifixion take place? How do we know? (At least 3 references)

4) What are the evidences that the tomb was *not* robbed? What convincing evidences are there for the Resurrection of Christ?

5) What are the main lessons we learn from the trip to Emmaus?

6) What does 1 John 3:2 mean? Explain it ***personally.***

Preparation for the Next Session:

Pray about the next book that the Lord would have you now study.
And pray about joining one of our on-line classes.

Group Discussion Questions: See the *Small Group Leaders* section of this workbook.

Discussion Questions for Small Group Leaders
The Gospel of Matthew

™Where two people agree, one is redundant∫

SESSION 1: Introduction and Chapter 1

1) In what way was the sin of Judah involving Tamar significant to the God's plan redemption?

2) How do we know the Bible is really true?

SESSION 2: Chapter 2

1) What was the "star" of Bethlehem? Why?

2) If "Pattern is Prophecy," how does one validate allegorical conjectures?

3) If Joseph, Mary, and Jesus returned to Nazareth after His circumcision and her purification (Luke 2:21,22,39), how does the flight to Egypt, pending Herod's death, fit in?

4) What special gift will be presented to Christ when He rules on Mt. Zion?

SESSION 3: Chapters 3 & 4

1) Was John the Baptist a member of "the Church"?

2) Is baptism a requirement for salvation?

3) How does one deal with temptations in their life?

4) Who is the "God of this world"? What does that imply regarding ***us***?

5) Contrast the founding the United States with our country today. What is the likelihood of returning to our roots? What should we be doing?

6) What is the cost of discipleship *today*?

SESSION 4: Chapter 5

1) How do you respond to someone who says "the Sermon on the Mount" is my religion?

2) Does a Christian have to keep the Law? Which ones?

3) How can you be the light in your community? The salt?

4) In what way were the Pharisees adversative examples?

5) In what several ways did Jesus fulfill the Mosaic Law?

SESSION 5: Chapters 6 & 7

1) What are the most important factors in *individual* prayer? In *corporate* or *community* prayer?

2) What are the most important factors in *giving*? In what way is *giving* a "spiritual gift"?

3) Contrast the need for planning with "taking no thought for the morrow."

4) Discuss the occurrence of "non-linearities" and how they should be anticipated or dealt with.

SESSION 6: Chapters 8 & 9

1) What did Jesus mean when He said, "Let the dead bury their dead"?

2) Was the "rebuking" of the sea (Matt. 8:26) only a figure of speech? What else might be implied?

3) What can we infer from the discovery of the ancient boat (sometimes called, the "Jesus Boat")?

4) In what way does Matthew seem to connect the woman with the issue of blood with the daughter of Jairus?

5) In terms of the ancient Jewish wedding ceremony as a prophetic type, what is the next event to be expected? Why?

SESSION 7: Chapters 10 & 11

1) How do the instructions given to the disciples in this session compare with the instructions to us today?

2) Was John the Baptist a fulfillment of the prophesied appearance of Elijah?

3) What did Jesus mean when He said, "Wisdom is justified of her children"?

SESSION 8: Chapter 12

1) Since Jesus is "Lord of the Sabbath," should a Christian observe the Sabbath Day? What pitfalls surround this issue?

2) How should we deal with traditions that are not Biblically based?

SESSION 9: Chapter 13

1) What personal applications can be drawn from the parables in this chapter? Which most impacted *you*?

2) Is there a relationship between the Seven Kingdom Parables and the Letters to the Seven Churches of Revelation? Is there a relationship with the epistles of Paul? Or the other epistles?

SESSION 10: Chapters 14 & 15

1) To the Hebrew mind, "Pattern is Prophecy." Is there a broader *typological* perspective suggested in these recent chapters?

2) How does modern Judaism compare with Mosaic Judaism (the Torah)?

SESSION 11: Chapters 16 & 17

1) Was the crucifixion on Friday? What difference does it make?

2) On what "rock" is the church built?

3) What are the "keys of the kingdom of heaven"?

4) How does one "lose his life" for Christ's sake?

5) Who are the Two Witnesses (and why)?

SESSION 12: Chapter 18

1) Discuss the steps to take, within the Body, for dealing with torts. What are examples of the failure of "due process" within the local church? What are the remedies needed?

2) What does it mean "to bind" or "to loose" in this session?

3) What does it mean to "become as little children"?

4) What does Matthew 18:7, "it must needs be that offences come; but woe to that man by whom the offence cometh," imply regarding free will?

5) Did Jesus really advocate amputation or mutilation as a means to avoid sin?

SESSION 13: Chapters 19 & 20

1) Discuss the implications and ramifications of divorce today.
What are the implications for remarriage?

2) What were the lessons Jesus gave concerning organizational hierarchy in the church?

3) What was the principal lesson of the householder's wage policies?

SESSION 14: Chapters 21: 1-11

1) How do we know where we are on God's timeline today?

2) What's significant of the blindness decreed upon Israel (Lk. 19:42)? What is today's relevance?

3) How do we know for certain that the prophecies of the Old Testament were documented several centuries ***before*** the New Testament period?

SESSION 15: Chapters 21 (Part 2) & 22

1) What are the personal lessons of the principal events in this session?

2) How are we confronted with a *dual* citizenship? What challenges can we anticipate in the future? How can we prepare for these challenges?

3) The coin bore Caesar's image; whose image do <u>we</u> bear? What is the application of this to each of us personally?

SESSION 16: Chapter 23

1) Why did God create us? Why did God redeem us?

2) Contrast each of the 8 woes on the Pharisees with the 8 beatitudes in Matthew 5. How are the 8 woes on the Pharisees relevant to us today? (Collectively and individually.)

3) How are the 6 woes of Isaiah 5 relevant to us today?

4) Do Christians need to tithe?

5) What events need to transpire a) Between the 69th and 70th "week"? b) Before the *harpazo?*

SESSION 17: Chapter 24 -- Part 1

1) How do we avoid being deceived?

2) What are the distinctions between Mosaic Judaism and the Judaism of today?

3) What is the "Abomination of Desolation" and its relevance to today.

4) Has the "Beginning of Sorrows" begun yet?

5) Which "generation shall not pass" away? To whom is this addressed?

6) What does Matthew 24:28 signify?

SESSION 18: Chapter 24 -- Part 2

1) Is the account in Luke 21 the same event as recorded in Matthew 24? How is this issue relevant?

2) Explain the parable of the fig tree and its relevance today.

3) What is the "doctrine of imminence" and how does it impact the views of: a) post-tribulationalism? b) mid-tribulationalism? c) pre-triubulationalism? d) amillennialism?

SESSION 19: Chapter 25

1) How do we apply the parable of the ten virgins to our own lives?

2) How do we apply the parable of ten talents to our own lives?

3) Who are "the brethren" in the Sheep and Goat Judgment? How do we apply this ***today*?**

SESSION 20: Chapter 26 -- Part 1

1) Should Christians observe Passover? What about the other feast days? What about Shabbat?

2) Was Judas responsible for having fulfilled prophecy? Why or why not?

SESSION 21: John 13 - 18

1) How should we observe "foot washing" today?

2) How is "loving one another" a ™*ew*∫ commandment? How is this different than Lev 19:18?

3) How are unfruitful vines pruned? What does that mean to us *today*?

4) Can you lose your salvation?

SESSION 22: Chapter 26 -- Part 2

1) What are main lessons we learn from Peter?

2) Are there any Peters among us? Are we similarly guilty of denials? Do we pray as we should?

SESSION 23: Chapter 27

1) What were *your* reactions to the Mel Gibson's move, *The Passion*? Strengths? Shortcomings? What two major issues did the movie *not* address?

2) In what way was the Crucifixion more of an *achievement* rather than a tragedy?

SESSION 24: Chapter 28

1) What is the real, practical, significance of the Resurrection to each of *us*, *today*?

2) Why do you think that so many seem to have had difficulty in recognizing the risen Lord?

3) What lessons might we glean from the denial—and reinstatement—of Peter?

Candidate Research Projects

For the truly dedicated

SESSION 1: Introduction and Chapter 1

1) Detail the process of the ancient Jewish wedding from betrothal to consummation, and its implications for the Believer today.

2) Trace the implications of the virgin birth from Genesis to Revelation.

3) Investigate the royal succession from David to Christ.

SESSION 2: Chapter 2

1) Study previous appearances of the Shekinah throughout the Scriptures.

2) Study the Hebrew Mazzeroth and how it apparently outlines God's Plan of Redemption. Also, relate it to the Twelve Tribes (and the 12 stars in Revelation 12).

3) Explore the history of the Persians, and the subsequent Parthians, in regards to their relationship with Israel.

SESSION 3: Chapters 3 & 4

1) Contrast Christian baptism with the use of the Hebrew *mikvah*.

2) List the *appearances* of the Holy Spirit in the Bible.

3) Compile examples in the Bible where mission focus was essential to success, and defendable distractions were Satan's tool.

4) Explore the founding of the United States in Scriptural terms. (Cf. *The Light and the Glory*, David Barton's Wallbuilders, et al.)

SESSION 4: Chapter 5

1) Explore the practices (positive as well as negative) of the Pharisees.

2) Explore the beliefs and practices of the Sadducees.

3) Trace the history of the Talmud, the Kabbalah, and the Hasidim. Who were the Karites, and how did they differ?

4) Review the Book of Romans in the light of this session. Review the Book of Galatians in this same light.

SESSION 5: Chapters 6 & 7

1) List the lessons learned from the prayer of John 17.

2) Summarize the lessons about the Law from Romans 1 thru 7.

3) Should Christians fast? Justify and explain. If so, what are the cautions and caveats?

SESSION 6: Chapters 8 & 9

1) Detail the elements of the ancient Jewish wedding ceremony: Where does it appear in the Bible as a prophetic type? What lessons can we infer?

2) How do we know that Jesus was *not* married?

3) Make a chart of the healing miracles in each of the four Gospels, contrasting the lessons of each.

4) Is there any case of a person dying in the presence of Christ? It is said that, after His resurrection, "He was only seen by loving eyes; He was only touched by loving hands." Is that true?

SESSION 7: Chapters 10 & 11

1) Explore the contrasts between the presentations of the Kingdom to:
   a) Israel
   b) The Church

2) How are they distinctive? In what ways are they mutually exclusive?

SESSION 8: Chapter 12

1) Investigate the arguments for worshipping on the 7th day and the 1st day of the week. Categorize the various views and their Biblical basis.

2) Investigate the various views of the day of the crucifixion: was it Friday? What are the implications of each alternative?

SESSION 9: Chapter 13

1) Are there patterns among the non-Pauline epistles of the New Testament and the patterns found in the Kingdom Parables or the Letters to the Seven Churches?

2) The fourth parable involved a woman; the fourth letter of the seven churches involved a woman. The fourth "judge" in the Book of Judges was Deborah. Are there other patterns of these parables in the Old Testament?

SESSION 10: Chapters 14 & 15

1) Investigate and chart the family of Herod and its impact on the New Testament period. Explore extra-Biblical sources: Josephus, et al.

2) Investigate the various forms of Judaism and their differences. (Compare them within a Biblical frame of reference.) How does the modern form of Kabbalah today relate to the Torah?

SESSION 11: Chapters 16 & 17

1) Compile list of appearances of the ***Shekinah*** in the Bible.

SESSION 12: Chapter 18

1) Investigate the application of "due process" among the various denominational organizations today, in light of Matthew 18:15-17.

SESSION 13: Chapters 19 & 20

1) Explore the implications of the Nicolaitans, their deeds and doctrines, in the church.

SESSION 14: Chapters 21:1-11

1) Explore the alternative views of "Replacement Theology" and their Biblical basis. How have these views impacted history?

2) Investigate the apparent "gaps" suggested throughout the Bible. How many can you find? What do they seem to have in common? What is their significance?

3) Explore the employment of 360-day years in the Biblical calendar, and other ancient cultures.

4) Explore the role of 360-day years in the prophecies in Ezekiel 4. Are they relevant to today?

5) Explore the possible near pass-bys of the Planet Mars and the potential impact on our understanding of the Long Day of Joshua in Joshua 10.

SESSION 15: Chapters 21 (part 2) & 22

1) Compile a comprehensive list of the idiomatic use of: a) stones b) mountains c) fig trees d) vineyard...throughout the Old and New Testaments.

SESSION 16: Chapter 23

1) In what ways do some people confuse Israel and the Church today? How are they similar? How are they distinct?

2) Does Jesus hold us accountable to know the prophetic Scriptures? (Cf. Luke 19:44; Matthew 24:15, et al.)

3) Compare the 6 woes of Isaiah 6 with the current status of America.

SESSION 17: Chapter 24 -- Part 1

1) Investigate the occasions when the "Abomination of Desolation" might have happened.

2) Explore the different views regarding the "beginning of sorrows."

3) Review the "preterist" views of Matthew 24, and their hermeneutica perspectives.

SESSION 18: Chapter 24 -- Part 2

1) Investigate the details of the events in Rome following Nero's death.

2) Investigate the details of the siege and fall of Jerusalem in 70 AD.

SESSION 19: Chapter 25

1) Draft an in-depth comparison of the three judgments above.

2) Draft a brief handbook for Christian stewardship.

SESSION 20: Chapters 26 -- Part 1

1) Trace the use of bread and wine through the Bible, prophetically.

2) Compile a comprehensive list of the ways that Passover was fulfilled in Jesus Christ.

3) The Mishna indicates that the wine at Passover is mixed with warm water. (*Mishna*, Pesach VII 13) Why?

SESSION 21: John 13 - 18

1) Contrast the use of the terms "Lord," "Master," etc., in the modern translations and paraphrases with the King James Version.

2) Summarize the views of a) The Calvinists b) The Arminians

3) Contrast the dangers to the church from: a) Outside: the world; b) Inside: from within the Body

SESSION 22: Chapter 26 -- Part 2

1) List the irregularities and illegalities in Jesus' trials.

SESSION 23: Chapter 27

1) Explore the original invention of crucifixion as form of execution. Where is it mentioned in the Old Testament?

2) Explore the background and destiny of Claudia Procula, wife of Pilate.

3) Explore the role of "thorns" in the Scriptures.

4) Explore the medical details of the Crucifixion of Christ.

5) List the Scriptural details that seem to support the Garden Tomb location. List the Scriptural details that seem to support the Church of Holy Sepulchre location.

SESSION 24: Chapter 28

1) Compile the most convincing evidences of the actual Resurrection of Christ.

2) Compile the various conjectures concerning the 153 fish in John 21:11.

Koinonia Institute

Online Course Instructions

1. Purchase a Campus Access Pass (CAP) that will give you FREE Tuition for all KHouse material courses. The CAP also provides many other benefits, for more information go to www.studycenter.com.
2. Once you have your CAP. go to www.studycenter.com and sign up for the course you would like to register for.
3. Make sure you purchase your course materials.

WEEKLY ROUTINE

1. Listen to your weekly course material.
2. Go to your class website and click the Discussion Questions link. There you will find a variety of questions and you will need to pick two of these to respond to. A text box is provided for you to write out your answers.
3. Anytime during the week you will need to go back to this section and select a classmate's post and respond to it. (Our Discussion Questions are subjective in nature and intended to create discussion – there are no right or wrong answers in this section).
4. At the end of each week there will be a short quiz that you will take online. For your weekly quiz you will usually find ten questions (true/false, matching and multiple choice).

This is the "typical" weekly schedule. At the end of your course you will take the Final. The Final is typically 50 – 100 questions, depending on the length of your class.

GRADING

25% of your grade will be the average of all your weekly quizzes combined
25% of your grade will be your participation with the Discussion Questions
50% of your grade will be your FINAL

A Final grade will then be issued and course credit given. If you are part of the KI program, you will receive credit that will go toward the pursuit of your Bronze, Silver or Gold Medallions. (For more information concerning the Medallion Program, go to www.studycenter.com and download our electronic KI Handbook and Course Catalog.)

If you are intending to use this course for credit at LBU then a five-to-ten page paper will also be assigned. When completed, you will either email or mail it to Koinonia Institute. It will be put in our files, along with your class transcript.

KOINONIA INSTITUTE

The Book of Matthew I BIB 529-1 3 credits
Sessions 1-12

The Book of Matthew II BIB 529-2 3 credits
Sessions 13-24

Koinonia Institute
P.O. Box D, Coeur d'Alene, Idaho 83816-0347
1-800-546-8731